READING and WRITING NUMBERS

Name_____

35,634	Thirty-five thousand, six hundred thirty-four
6,000,900	Six million, nine hundred
200,000,004	Two hundred million, four

Read the following numbers.

1. 900,702   3,004,081   9,421,620
2. 7,490,378   89,500,100   206,220,800
3. 8,004,500   69,521,001   260,090,210

Write the correct numeral for each number.

1. Five hundred sixty-two thousand, one hundred seventy-four _____

2. Two hundred million, five hundred eighteen thousand, seven hundred thirty-six _____

3. Sixty-five billion, two hundred seventy million, nine hundred forty-eight thousand, three hundred one _____

4. Nine trillion, four hundred sixty billion, seven hundred twelve million, nineteen thousand, five hundred three _____

Challenge
Rearrange each group of numbers from smallest to largest.

| 37,049,757 | 36,049,957 | 34,049,858 |
| _____ | _____ | _____ |

| 36,491,956 | 36,126,851 | 36,490,856 |
| _____ | _____ | _____ |

PLACE VALUE

Ten-Thousands	Thousands	Hundreds	Tens	Ones
8	**8**	**8**	**8**	**8**

Look carefully at the number above, note that **8** has a different value, and that this value depends upon the place the figure holds in a number. Each **8** is 10 times the value of the **8** to the right of it.

The value of a figure depends upon the place it holds in a number.

1. In the number 5,356,919, what is the value of each number?

   5 means ____5,000,000____

   3 means _____300,000_____

   5 means _____

   6 means _____

   9 means _____

   1 means _____

   9 means _____

2. In each set, draw a circle around the largest number. Underline the smallest number.

8,651,233	1,863,741,908	5,423,416,814
8,653,234	1,853,743,907	5,423,416,014
8,555,229	1,863,745,906	5,423,416,804
6,439,016,213	105,023,010,001	2,416,029,786
7,230,104,203	105,003,010,001	2,406,029,786
6,439,015,213	105,023,000,001	2,410,009,786

2

CHECKING ADDITION and SUBTRACTION

Name_____

	Example	Check	
	584	297	Check addition by
	+ 297	+ 584	adding in reverse.
	881	881	
	701	235	Check subtraction with
	− 466	+ 466	addition.
	235	701	

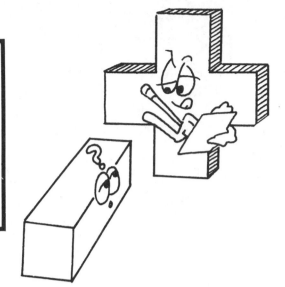

Check each problem for accuracy. Write **T** for true and **F** for false.

1. 28,153
    − 17,745 _____
    10,408

2. 49,853
    + 83,289 _____
    132,132

3. 8,466
    + 7,907 _____
    16,373

4. 84,542
    − 9,368 _____
    75,174

5. 642,017
    − 568,726 _____
    73,291

6. 7,431
    + 6,214 _____
    14,745

7. 52,814
    + 7,623 _____
    60,437

8. 74,222
    + 6,787 _____
    80,419

9. 872
    − 593 _____
    379

10. 8,466
     + 7,907 _____
     16,373

11. 3,001
     − 597 _____
     2,403

12. 7,210
     + 6,143 _____
     13,353

ADDITION

Add.

1.
```
   508,209
    41,642
     9,021
       100
 +     395
```

2.
```
   986,412
    79,843
     2,764
       963
 +     229
```

3.
```
   870,304
    90,427
     8,002
       734
 +     895
```

4.
```
 7,007,421
 3,900,340
   740,070
 5,422,009
 +   7,080
```

5.
```
   305,208
    70,040
     4,040
       721
 +     603
```

6.
```
 7,002,350
   408,902
    75,700
     8,060
 +     476
```

7.
```
 5,003,820
   408,502
    42,700
     7,060
 +     921
```

8.
```
 8,007,730
   408,403
    71,900
     9,090
 +     520
```

9.
```
   904,501
   621,423
    72,432
     8,290
 +     726
```

10.
```
     8,395
    21,987
    96,374
    34,910
 + 84,795
```

11.
```
    64,153
     2,934
    34,900
    63,280
 + 23,962
```

12.
```
    21,987
    46,832
    92,138
    31,629
 +   4,796
```

13.
```
   239,600
    84,795
   294,100
    64,739
 + 83,271
```

14.
```
    34,762
    29,788
    39,979
    68,394
 + 72,591
```

15.
```
    92,436
    96,842
    21,943
    76,429
 + 10,402
```

16.
```
    92,138
    31,629
    47,962
    34,316
 + 18,213
```

ADDITION

Add.

1.   8,539
  + 4,678

2.   9,536
  + 5,791

3.   7,648
  + 5,488

4.   7,849
  + 9,679

5.   8,597
  + 6,345

6.   6,758
  + 4,979

7.   9,378
  + 3,998

8.   5,875
  + 9,569

9.   9,585
  + 7,080

10.   5,938
  + 6,894

11.   31,629
  +   4,796

12.   6,758
  + 2,643

13.   865,346
  + 498,688

14.   987,651
  + 598,798

15.   753,470
  + 472,181

16.   675,526
  + 598,641

Challenge
Arrange in columns and add.

1. 600 + 80 + 45 + 950 + 75 + 189 = _____

2. 121 + 426 + 986 + 21 + 45 + 278 = _____

3. 926 + 871 + 49 + 867 + 21 + 986 = _____

4. 857 + 276 + 86 + 924 + 72 + 694 = _____

5. 791 + 426 + 63 + 261 + 83 + 749 = _____

ADDITION

1.
```
   921,206
    92,126
     4,201
       960
 +     420
```

2.
```
   629,437
    76,829
     9,100
       265
 +     786
```

3.
```
   776,824
    81,429
     9,600
       422
 +     861
```

4.
```
   878,204
    26,749
     1,322
       687
 +     682
```

5.
```
   286,400
    63,721
     7,834
       821
 +      20
```

6.
```
   999,999
    88,888
     7,777
       666
 +     555
```

7.
```
   426,699
    72,432
     6,210
       427
 +     563
```

8.
```
   291,426
    63,487
     7,648
       876
 +     635
```

9.
```
 4,002,330
   704,906
    72,700
     9,160
 +     580
```

10.
```
 1,008,400
 4,900,640
   740,160
 8,440,003
 +   8,102
```

11.
```
 6,005,600
 7,009,420
   560,051
 4,328,008
 +   6,321
```

12.
```
 3,005,600
   205,320
    71,426
     2,600
 +     126
```

13.
```
 9,005,720
   480,302
    63,500
     8,429
 +     624
```

14.
```
    12,000
       250
     4,603
       186
 +     404
```

15.
```
     5,001
       105
    20,405
     4,631
 +     221
```

16.
```
 7,864,200
   695,154
    86,423
     1,500
 +     786
```

17.
```
    94,983
    69,787
    74,978
    68,666
    39,789
 + 87,878
```

18.
```
    79,935
    86,940
    30,979
    85,398
    74,297
 + 68,849
```

REVIEW

Name_____

Follow the directions to find the hidden treasure at the bottom of the Indian Ocean. If you make no errors, the final answer will be **0**.

0 Begin

Add 91.

Add 421.

Subtract 209.

Add 648.

Subtract 63.

Add 12.

Add 76.

Subtract 923.

Add 47.

Subtract 100.

IT WAS NOTHING.

End
0

Treasure

MAGIC SQUARES

Name_____

The sum of each row, column and diagonal is the same in a magic square. Fill in the blanks.

1.

20		4
9	10	17

2.

2		6
	5	
		8

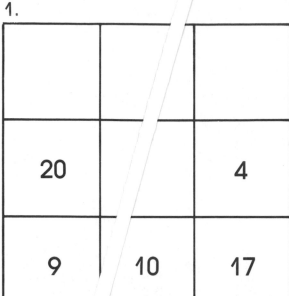

3.

	19	
7	11	
	3	13

4.

12		
44	25	6

Challenge
Add.

1. 40,214 + 921,420,623 + 6,426,004 + 7,201,403 = _____

2. 104 + 4,900,600,429 + 6,216,777,014 + 386 = _____

3. 9,004,276 + 621,924,104 + 666 + 7,871 = _____

ESTIMATING SUMS

Name_____

Rounding is an easy way to find out how many in all.

Nearest Ten.		Nearest Hundred		Nearest Thousand	
39	40	421	400	989	1,000
+48	+50	+499	+500	+1,421	+1,000
	90		900		2,000

1.   86
     + 43
     90
     +40

2.   21
     + 89

3.   98
     + 32

4.   836
     + 295

5.   821
     + 69

6.   271
     + 126

7.   1,423
     + 989

8.   8,321
     + 7,894

9.   6,431
     + 2,986

10.   793
     + 16

11.   2,426
     + 149

12.   621
     + 599

13.   1,639
     + 403

14.   8,798
     + 8,640

15.   9,198
     + 8,102

Challenge
Michael went to the Sports Center. He bought a helmet for $29.99, a sweat shirt for $9.49 and a pair of running shoes for $52.99. Estimate what Michael spent.

SUBTRACTION

Name_____

437 − 164	872 − 439	396 − 199	600 − 347	906 − 469	1300 − 76
6407 − 529	3400 − 2108	7021 − 3764	9003 − 7685	676 − 208	3604 − 2786
8400 − 4999	1203 − 596	6700 − 3985	1608 − 567	5702 − 3986	1500 − 59

Monster Maze

Shade in answers below to find a path to the castle. There is more than one way to get there.

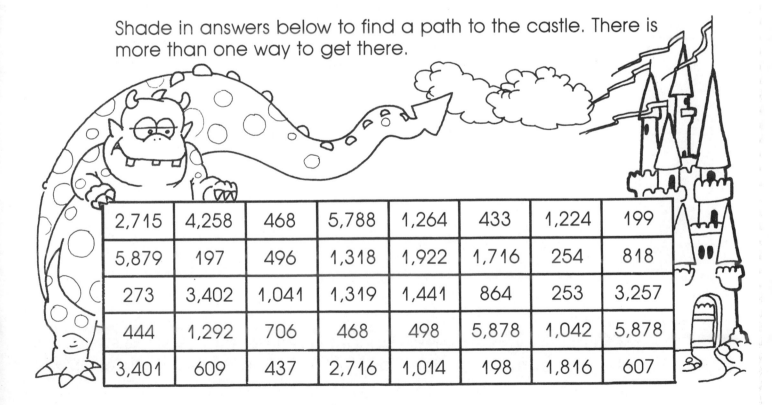

2,715	4,258	468	5,788	1,264	433	1,224	199
5,879	197	496	1,318	1,922	1,716	254	818
273	3,402	1,041	1,319	1,441	864	253	3,257
444	1,292	706	468	498	5,878	1,042	5,878
3,401	609	437	2,716	1,014	198	1,816	607

SUBTRACTION

Name_____

Work the baseball problems. Each answer found on the bat represents a homerun. How many homeruns were hit? _____

```
62111    1184    37785    6135    322    5631    2371
                 3091     37786   2118   5256
                          5646    2615   4431   7287
```

$$3118 - 1207$$

$$9893 - 7521$$

$$9217 - 375$$

$$7354 - 4739$$

$$5806 - 560$$

$$5008 - 4201$$

$$3468 - 2384$$

$$7975 - 805$$

$$7672 - 4291$$

$$6760 - 2125$$

$$90{,}006 - 52{,}221$$

$$4382 - 761$$

$$8779 - 5137$$

$$1725 - 1413$$

$$9372 - 3741$$

$$4537 - 2519$$

$$1{,}834{,}216 - 1{,}772{,}105$$

$$3448 - 2374$$

$$7352 - 65$$

$$5738 - 92$$

$$43{,}026 - 219$$

$$9987 - 3852$$

$$6172 - 3081$$

$$4357 - 26$$

$$8710 - 14$$

ZEROS in SUBTRACTION

Name_____

6,040 − 406 5,634	6,000 − 407 5,593	6,000 − 400 5,600	6,004 − 407 5,597

Subtract and check.

1. 402.01
    − 20.40

2. 606.09
    − 40.80

3. 800.05
    − 50.09

4. 605.90
    − 50.70

5. 8,050
    −   508

6. 8,000
    −   406

7. 40.30
    − 1.06

8. 7,060
    −   708

9. 90,000
    − 4,638

10. 70,000
     − 2,975

11. 60,004
     − 5,007

12. 80,406
     − 7,012

13. 80,002
     − 3,008

14. 40,006
     − 3,216

15. 3,000
     − 107

16. 70,081
     − 4,200

17. 60,027
     − 55,575

18. 68,370
     − 6,400

19. 64,900
     − 63,289

20. 9,489
     − 6,766

21. 46,000
     − 9,826

22. 60,000
     − 54,789

23. 98,900
     − 83,721

24. 46,920
     − 8,649

ZEROS in SUBTRACTION

Name_____

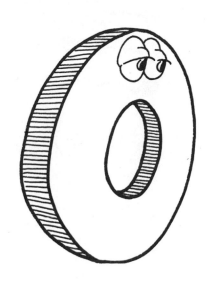
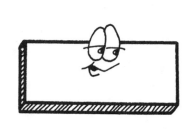
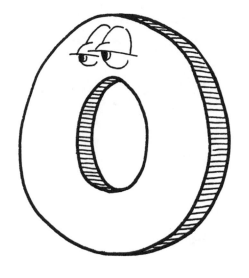

1. 2,000,000
    − 366,728

2. 4,000,000
    − 279,634

3. 6,000,000
    − 173,825

4. 8,000,000
    − 761,642

5. 800,000
    − 265,529

6. 5,000,000
    − 563,275

7. 8,000,000
    − 581,463

8. 6,000,000
    − 832,479

9. 20,000,000
    − 2,656,491

10. 60,000,000
    − 5,953,861

11. 40,000,000
    − 1,564,299

12. 700,000
    − 462,138

13. 900,000
    − 276,421

14. 50,000,000
    − 42,163,291

15. 10,000,000
    − 4,986,721

16. 400,000
    − 361,248

17. 300,000
    − 296,326

18. 70,000,000
    − 54,321,631

19. 2,000,000
    − 622,431

20. 200,000
    − 168,429

REVIEW: + ×

Name_____

What is each game's score? ● Tanya ○ Noel

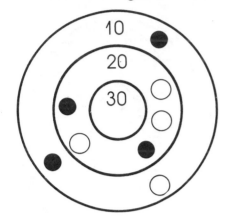

Tanya _____

Noel _____

Tanya _____

Noel _____

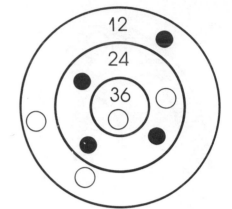

Tanya _____

Noel _____

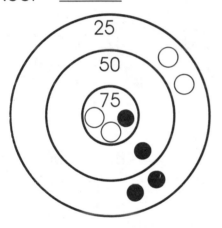

Tanya _____

Noel _____

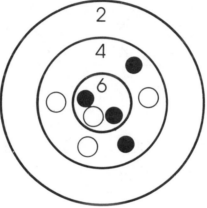

Tanya _____

Noel _____

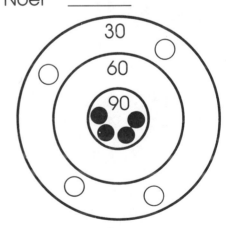

Tanya _____

Noel _____

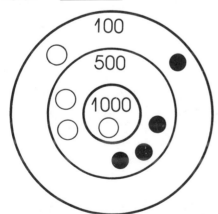

Tanya _____

Noel _____

Tanya _____

Noel _____

Tanya _____

Noel _____

Total points for Tanya _____   Total points for Noel _____   Who won? _____

MULTIPLES

Name_____

Multiples express multiplication and division facts.

> The multiples of 6 as far as 6 × 9 are:
> 6, 12, 18, 24, 30, 36, 42, 48 and 54.
>
> The multiples of 9 as far as 9 × 9 are:
> 9, 18, 27, 36, 45, 54, 63, 72 and 81.
>
> When we find the above multiples of 6 and 9, we can compare and find that some multiples are alike.
>
> Therefore, 18, 36 and 54 contain 6 and also 9.
> Then, 18 is the Least Common Multiple of 6 and 9.
> L.C.M. means Least Common Multiple.

1. Write the first 8 multiples of 3, 4 and 6.

   3, _____, _____, _____, _____, _____, _____, _____

   4, _____, _____, _____, _____, _____, _____, _____

   6, _____, _____, _____, _____, _____, _____, _____
2. What are the common multiples of 3, 4 and 6?

   _____ and _____
3. What is the L.C.M. of 3, 4 and 6? _____

4. What is the smallest number that is exactly divisible by each pair?

   a. 5 and 3 _____   e. 4, 5 and 10 _____

   b. 7 and 2 _____   f. 4, 6 and 9 _____

   c. 6 and 9 _____   g. 2, 4 and 8 _____

   d. 3, 6 and 8 _____   h. 5, 6 and 15 _____

5. 40 is a multiple of 8 and _____;

   2 and _____; 10 and _____.

FACTOR TREES
Multiply.

Name_____

1.
3 × 3 × 2
□ × 2
□

2.
3 × 5 × 3
□ × □
□

3.
□ × 2 × 3
6 × □
□

4.
□ × □ × 5
□ × □
20

5.
□ × 2 × 4
10 × □
□

6.
3 × 5 × 2
□ × □
□

7.
□ × □ × □ × □
9 × 9 × □
81 × 9
□

8.
3 × 3 × 2 × 2
□ × □ × □
□ × □
□

9.
2 × □ × 2 × □
4 × □ × 9
□ × □
□

10.
2 × 5 × □
□ × 7
□

11.
5 × 5 × 2
□ × □
□

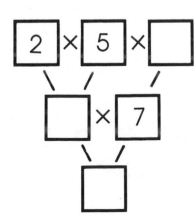

Math IF8744

20

© 1990 Instructional Fair, Inc.

MULTIPLICATION

Name_____

The pioneers have just had their first major set-back. All four wheels fell off their covered wagon going through the dangerous Rocky Mountains. You can help them put the wheels back on by multiplying each complete wheel.

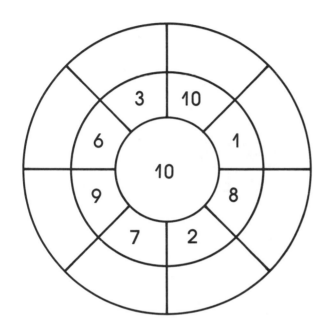

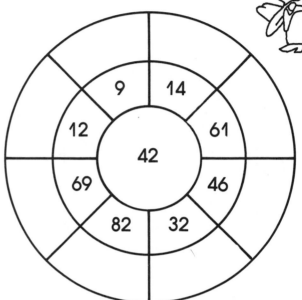

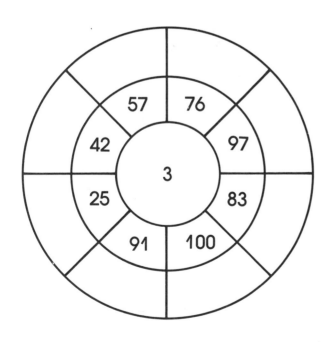

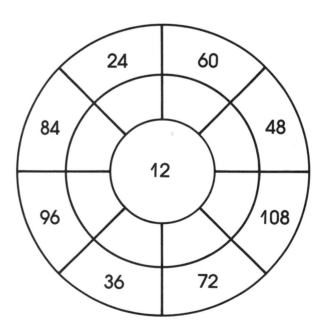

MULTIPLICATION FACTS

Name_____

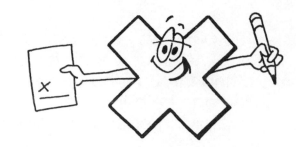

Multiplication facts 2 through 9

×	8
6	48
2	16
1	8

×	9
8	
2	
6	

×	6
7	
2	
8	

×	2
8	
6	
9	

×	4
6	
7	
9	

×	7
3	
6	
8	

×	5
7	
3	
5	

×	3
8	
6	
4	

×	8
4	
9	
7	

×	4
4	
8	
5	

×	8
5	
7	
8	

×	6
9	
6	
4	

×	9
7	
5	
4	

×	5
9	
6	
4	

×	7
7	
3	
9	

×	4
6	
2	
8	

×	2
7	
5	
4	

×	6
5	
3	
1	

×	9
3	
1	
6	

×	8
3	
6	
4	

×	7
9	
5	
2	

MULTIPLICATION

Name_____

The arrows show which two numbers to multiply
and where to write the answer.

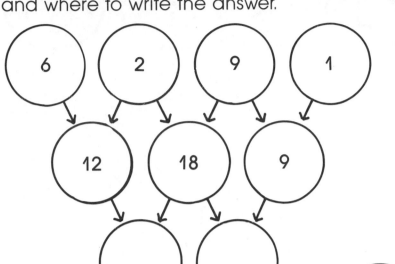

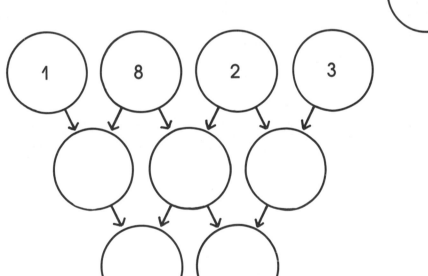

MULTIPLICATION

Name_____

Remember: Any number times zero equals zero.

1. 905
    × 7

2. 800
    × 9

3. 804
    × 6

4. 470
    × 8

5. 709
    × 6

6. 500
    × 6

7. 900
    × 8

8. 608
    × 6

9. 428
    × 6

10. 890
    × 5

11. 720
    × 4

12. 420
    × 5

13. 576
    × 2

14. 530
    × 7

15. 970
    × 3

16. 700
    × 9

17. 638
    × 6

18. 497
    × 8

19. 982
    × 7

20. 631
    × 7

21. 707
    × 6

22. 940
    × 8

23. 290
    × 6

24. 874
    × 0

25. 9204
    × 7

26. 8649
    × 8

27. 4309
    × 7

28. 6402
    × 5

THREE-PLACE MULTIPLIER

Name_____

I.	468	Multiplicand
	× 375	Multiplier
	2340	1st Partial Product
	3276	2nd Partial Product
	1404	3rd Partial Product
	175500	Product

II.	987
	× 645
	4935
	3948
	5922
	636615

III.	850
	× 470
	000
	5150
	3400
	391500

1.   804
        × 408

2.   700
        × 840

3.   500
        × 902

4.   608
        × 240

5.   678
        × 386

6.   762
        × 691

7.   398
        × 421

8.   709
        × 284

9.   703
        × 307

10.   843
         × 658

11.   504
         × 405

12.   200
         × 607

13.   874
         × 981

14.   426
         × 721

15.   638
         × 247

16.   150
         × 342

MULTIPLICATION

Name_____

You choose the color of each flower's petals.

Petals with an 8 in the answer are _____.

Petals with a 5 in the answer are _____.

Petals with a 3 in the answer are _____.

Petals with a 7 in the answer are _____.

Math IF8744

26

© 1990 Instructional Fair, Inc.

MULTIPLICATION

Name_____

Can you help me complete the web? To fill in the last ring, multiply the number in the center and keep multiplying in a straight line from the center. Remember, a spider's lifetime is short, so don't waste any time.

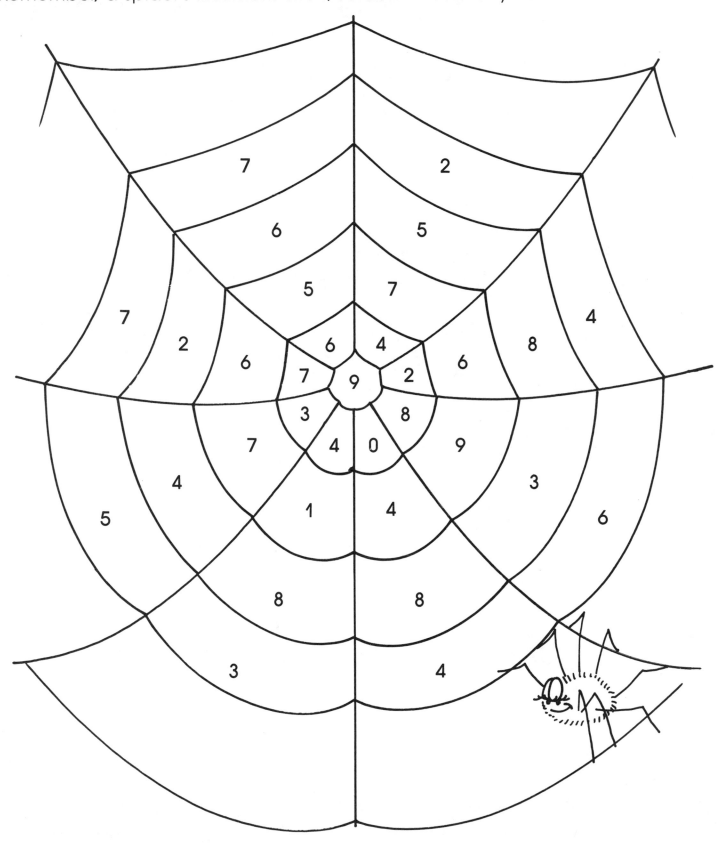

DIVISION: 1-Digit Divisor

Name_____

Work problems. Give the clowns with remainders a happy face 😊. Give the clowns without remainders a sad face ☹️.

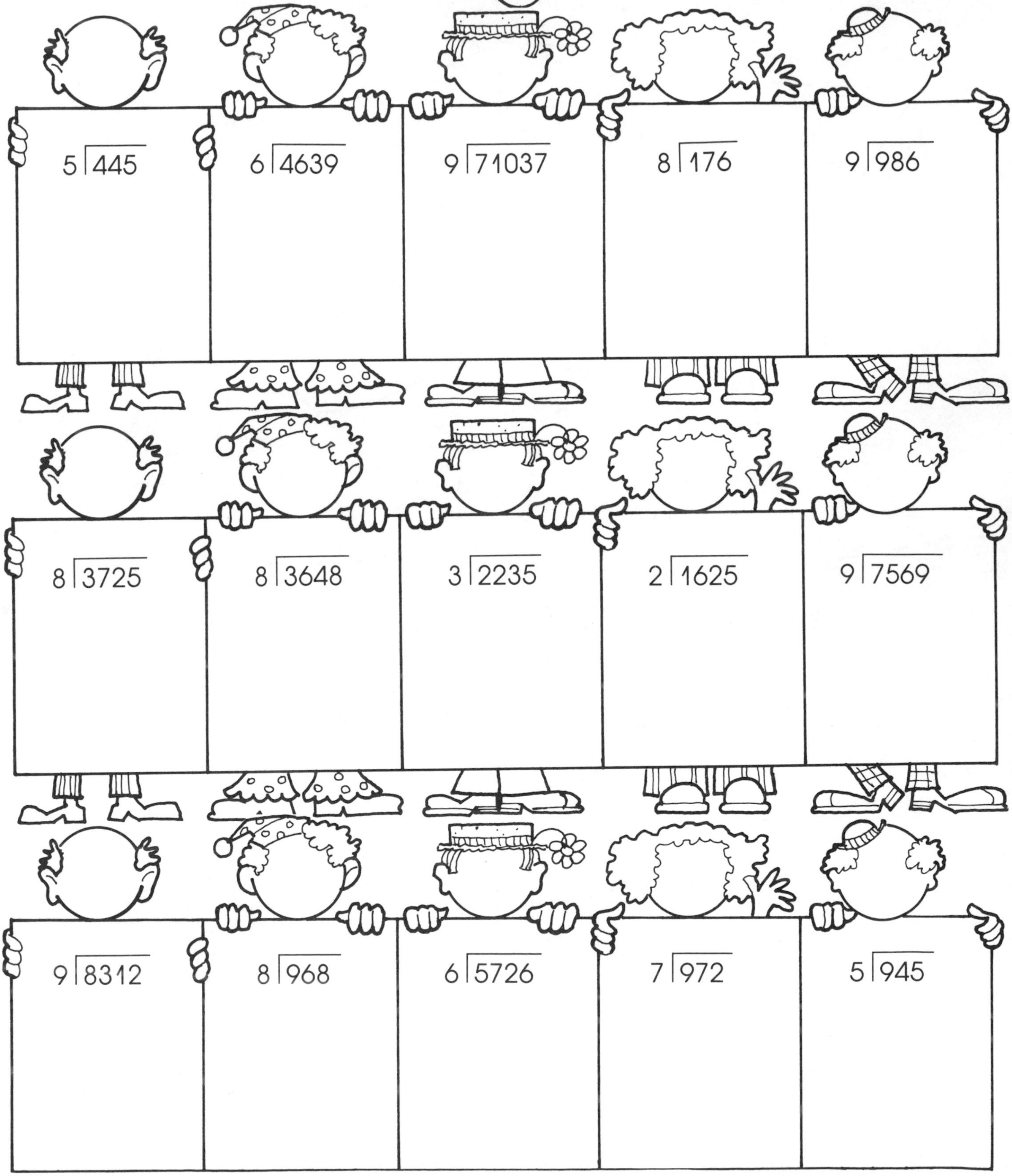

$5\overline{)445}$	$6\overline{)4639}$	$9\overline{)71037}$	$8\overline{)176}$	$9\overline{)986}$

$8\overline{)3725}$	$8\overline{)3648}$	$3\overline{)2235}$	$2\overline{)1625}$	$9\overline{)7569}$

$9\overline{)8312}$	$8\overline{)968}$	$6\overline{)5726}$	$7\overline{)972}$	$5\overline{)945}$

DIVISION

Name_____

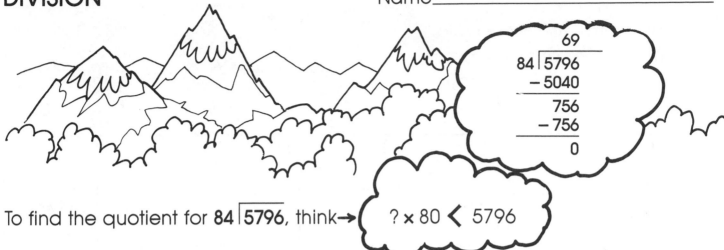

$$\begin{array}{r} 69 \\ 84\overline{)5796} \\ -5040 \\ \hline 756 \\ -756 \\ \hline 0 \end{array}$$

To find the quotient for $84\overline{)5796}$, think→ ($? \times 80 < 5796$)

1. $40\overline{)2560}$

2. $50\overline{)2150}$

3. $31\overline{)9362}$

4. $62\overline{)12,400}$

5. $51\overline{)1020}$

6. $35\overline{)1050}$

7. $84\overline{)6720}$

8. $26\overline{)1638}$

9. $12\overline{)372}$

10. $29\overline{)2465}$

11. $90\overline{)7020}$

12. $60\overline{)4560}$

13. $30\overline{)2460}$

14. $49\overline{)294}$

15. $80\overline{)640}$

16. $7\overline{)210}$

DIVISION: 2-Digit Divisor

Name_____

Work problems. To find path to bottom of cave, answers match problem number. Shade path.

1. $74 \overline{\smash{)}222}$	2. $95 \overline{\smash{)}285}$	3. $75 \overline{\smash{)}300}$	4. $54 \overline{\smash{)}270}$	5. $63 \overline{\smash{)}252}$	6. $89 \overline{\smash{)}534}$	7. $22 \overline{\smash{)}198}$
8. $84 \overline{\smash{)}504}$	9. $52 \overline{\smash{)}416}$	10. $84 \overline{\smash{)}924}$	11. $35 \overline{\smash{)}385}$	12. $93 \overline{\smash{)}1116}$	13. $69 \overline{\smash{)}897}$	14. $95 \overline{\smash{)}1140}$
15. $63 \overline{\smash{)}882}$	16. $35 \overline{\smash{)}525}$	17. $21 \overline{\smash{)}357}$	18. $73 \overline{\smash{)}1314}$	19. $36 \overline{\smash{)}648}$	20. $34 \overline{\smash{)}782}$	21. $44 \overline{\smash{)}792}$
22. $66 \overline{\smash{)}1386}$	23. $99 \overline{\smash{)}2277}$	24. $24 \overline{\smash{)}576}$	25. $38 \overline{\smash{)}874}$	26. $84 \overline{\smash{)}2268}$	27. $28 \overline{\smash{)}672}$	28. $33 \overline{\smash{)}858}$
29. $37 \overline{\smash{)}962}$	30. $35 \overline{\smash{)}1050}$	31. $46 \overline{\smash{)}966}$	32. $27 \overline{\smash{)}837}$	33. $21 \overline{\smash{)}987}$	34. $29 \overline{\smash{)}928}$	35. $16 \overline{\smash{)}736}$
	36. $63 \overline{\smash{)}2268}$	37. $62 \overline{\smash{)}2294}$	38. $13 \overline{\smash{)}494}$	39. $18 \overline{\smash{)}774}$	40. $78 \overline{\smash{)}3276}$	
	41. $78 \overline{\smash{)}3432}$	42. $24 \overline{\smash{)}1008}$	43. $53 \overline{\smash{)}2544}$			

30

DIVISION: 2-Digit Divisor

Name _____

Work soccer problems. Each answer found in a team's net represents a score for that team. What was the game score?

Red team _____

Blue team _____

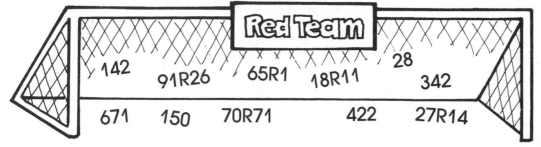

Red Team

142   91R26   65R1   18R11   28   342

671   150   70R71   422   27R14

37 ⟌18241   89 ⟌25276   27 ⟌743   15 ⟌405   62 ⟌984   45 ⟌28260

42 ⟌5761   35 ⟌7623   12 ⟌7641   65 ⟌8125   9 ⟌71037   96 ⟌81312

73 ⟌9863   79 ⟌75208   27 ⟌6529   42 ⟌28182   44 ⟌38412   81 ⟌48114

8 ⟌3648   56 ⟌5178   84 ⟌4361   36 ⟌5436   97 ⟌3522   61 ⟌5536

56 ⟌7952   89 ⟌4895   37 ⟌4477   72 ⟌5181   66 ⟌4291   26 ⟌7644

47 ⟌5358   73 ⟌5181   46 ⟌3923   18 ⟌6156   26 ⟌479   18 ⟌7614

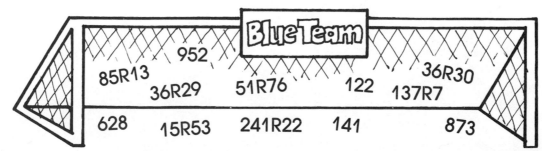

Blue Team

952   85R13   36R29   51R76   122   36R30   137R7

628   15R53   241R22   141   873

DIVISION

Name_____

```
        423 R 4                    420
   35 )14809              34 )14280
     -140                   -136
       80                     68
      -70                    -68
      109                      0
     -105
        4
```

1.
81)3726

2.
83)3158

3.
76)68413

4.
93)84309

5.
95)3990

6.
34)17714

7.
83)1826

8.
75)15009

9.
57)22800

10.
43)10750

11.
58)18690

12.
33)82500

13.
64)17740

14.
32)82800

15.
32)20510

16.
65)52000

DIVISION: 2-Digit Divisor

Name_____

Work problems. Shade in the letters of those problems that have remainders to reveal the "ancient one".

A. 42 ⟌ 8799

B. 33 ⟌ 9278

C. 72 ⟌ 38952

D. 43 ⟌ 28939

E. 52 ⟌ 336

F. 26 ⟌ 16822

G. 58 ⟌ 22388

H. 27 ⟌ 743

I. 57 ⟌ 20406

J. 35 ⟌ 296

K. 62 ⟌ 984

L. 42 ⟌ 5761

M. 38 ⟌ 8056

N. 36 ⟌ 28404

O. 35 ⟌ 7623

P. 62 ⟌ 6735

Q. 26 ⟌ 1664

R. 46 ⟌ 419

S. 84 ⟌ 6552

T. 17 ⟌ 9741

U. 52 ⟌ 4628

V. 17 ⟌ 6145

W. 41 ⟌ 8173

X. 39 ⟌ 5304

Y. 66 ⟌ 6930

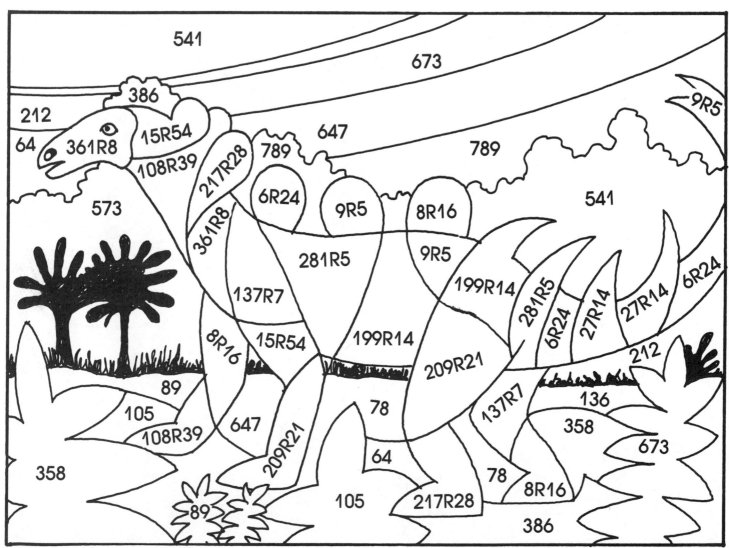

DIVISION

Name_____

Divide each problem. Draw a line connecting each problem to its answer.

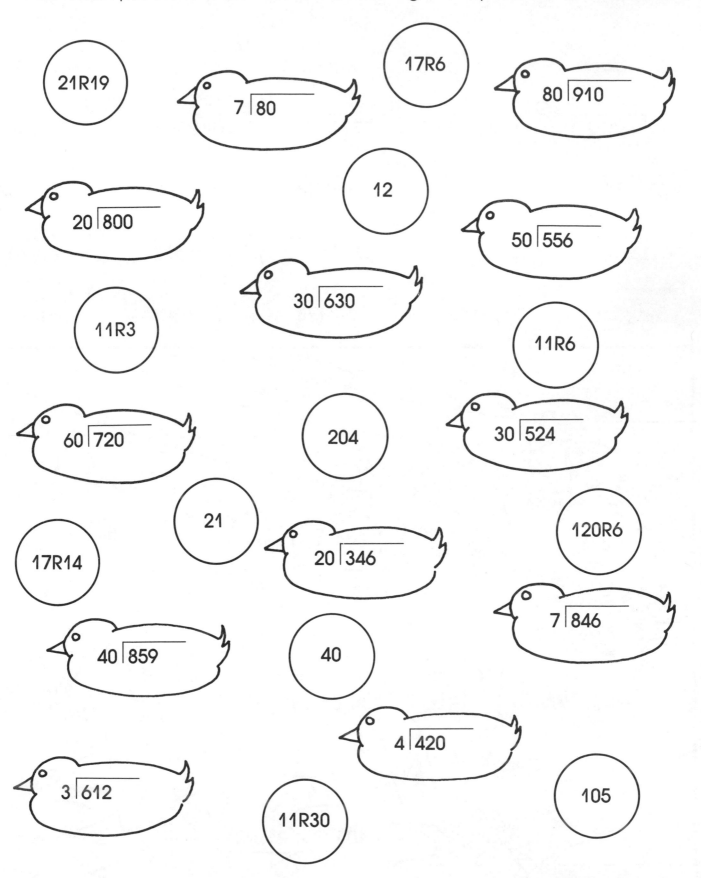

21R19

7 ⟌ 80

17R6

80 ⟌ 910

20 ⟌ 800

12

50 ⟌ 556

30 ⟌ 630

11R3

11R6

60 ⟌ 720

204

30 ⟌ 524

21

120R6

17R14

20 ⟌ 346

7 ⟌ 846

40 ⟌ 859

40

4 ⟌ 420

3 ⟌ 612

11R30

105

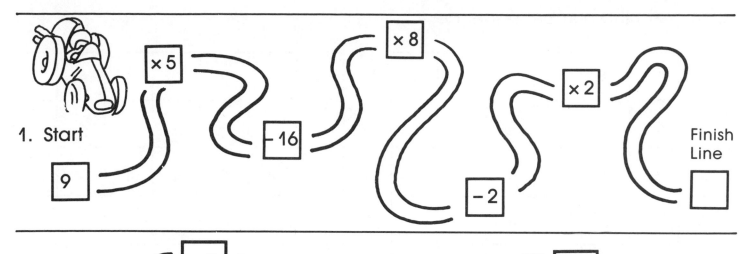

1. Start

9   ×5   −16   ×8   −2   ×2   Finish Line ▢

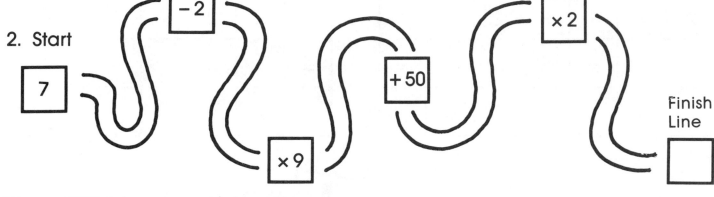

2. Start

7   −2   ×9   +50   ×2   Finish Line ▢

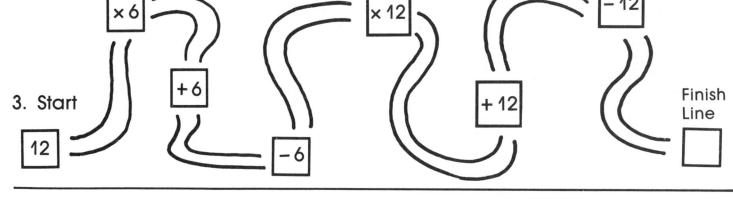

3. Start

12   ×6   +6   −6   ×12   +12   −12   Finish Line ▢

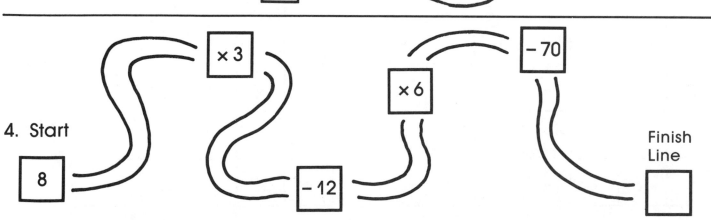

4. Start

8   ×3   −12   ×6   −70   Finish Line ▢

Name_____

Complete the number sentences.

8	×	3	×	2	=	
÷		÷		÷		÷
2	×	1	×	1	=	
÷		÷		÷		÷
2	×	3	×	2	=	
=		=		=		=
	×		×		=	

4	×	2	×	4	=	
÷		÷		÷		÷
1	×	1	×	1	×	
÷		÷		÷		÷
4	×	2	×	1	=	
=		=		=		=
	×		×		=	

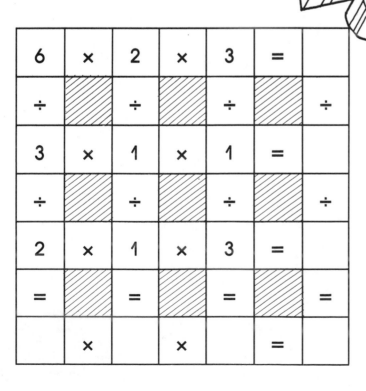

6	×	2	×	3	=	
÷		÷		÷		÷
3	×	1	×	1	=	
÷		÷		÷		÷
2	×	1	×	3	=	
=		=		=		=
	×		×		=	

5	×	8	×	2	=	
÷		÷		÷		÷
1	×	4	×	2	=	
÷		÷		÷		÷
5	×	2	×	1	=	
=		=		=		=
	×		×		=	

Name_____

Start at the bottom of the steps. Write your answer at the top.

1.
÷ 10
+ 3
× 9
÷ 5
+ 6
÷ 9
81

2.
÷ 9
− 2
× 7
÷ 8
+ 1
× 7
9

3.
× 7
÷ 8
+ 6
÷ 2
× 5
+ 4
16

4.
+ 2
× 2
+ 2
÷ 2
× 6
+ 4
2

5.
÷ 5
+ 4
× 8
÷ 7
+ 5
÷ 7
63

6.
÷ 2
× 4
+ 10
÷ 12
× 2
× 2
6

7.
× 8
− 2
+ 2
÷ 9
+ 8
× 8
8

8.
+ 3
÷ 9
+ 9
× 2
÷ 9
× 9
9

37

BASIC REVIEW: + − × ÷

Name_____

Work problems. Use answers to complete number crosses.

ACROSS

A.	701 −582	C.	2615 −2569	D.	882 − 99

DOWN

A.	467 −333	B.	1123 − 153	C.	707 −664

ACROSS

E.	49876 + 1265	H.	1243 +3040

I. 17
    18
    35
    12
     3
     5

DOWN

E.	26 +26	F.	95 +94	G.	63 +76

     1
     2
     4
   + 2

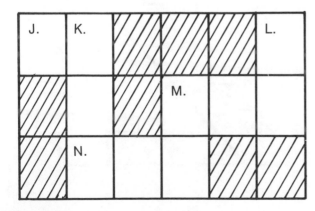

ACROSS

J. 12⟌852   M. 2⟌372   N. 3⟌987

DOWN

K. 5⟌765   L. 3⟌138   M. 5⟌95

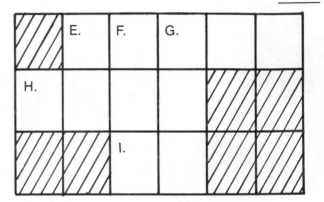

ACROSS

O.	34 ×34	S.	17 × 2	T.	43 ×16

DOWN

P.	29 × 6	Q.	26 ×26	R.	38 ×26

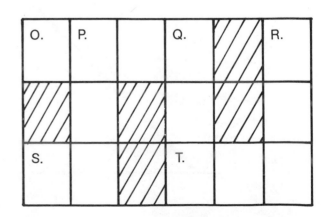

MATH WORDS

Name_____

There are at least 30 words to seek and find.

m	u	l	t	i	p	l	i	e	r	t	r	o	p	g	a	l	l	o	n
x	i	v	x	m	z	s	v	e	a	y	x	z	s	e	t	w	o	o	n
v	o	l	u	m	e	q	l	a	d	b	e	e	l	g	n	a	i	r	t
d	i	o	l	i	v	u	t	l	i	r	m	e	t	e	r	t	r	k	o
z	e	r	a	i	r	a	u	x	t	i	n	c	i	r	c	l	e	c	i
g	e	o	m	e	t	r	y	e	t	a	d	d	f	a	c	t	l	i	n
j	a	r	x	t	z	e	r	o	o	t	h	i	r	d	e	n	u	t	u
v	x	d	i	v	i	s	i	o	n	i	n	t	e	g	e	r	r	s	m
t	d	i	g	i	t	s	c	o	t	t	b	u	s	h	u	r	u	d	e
z	t	n	e	c	r	e	p	v	c	u	b	e	t	x	l	z	l	r	r
n	x	a	v	e	r	a	g	e	s	n	x	f	i	x	a	t	a	a	a
o	z	l	e	n	g	t	h	s	s	u	n	i	m	v	v	a	r	y	l
i	m	n	a	r	e	a	n	t	m	x	g	r	a	p	h	o	r	t	u
t	z	t	a	m	u	l	t	i	p	l	y	z	t	i	n	u	n	x	l
c	m	a	d	d	i	t	i	o	n	u	m	b	e	r	v	i	n	c	e
a	g	r	a	p	x	c	o	n	e	d	p	e	r	i	m	e	t	e	r
r	c	y	l	i	n	d	e	r	e	a	s	o	n	o	g	a	x	e	h
f	o	u	r	t	h	v	t	d	i	v	i	s	o	r	e	a	r	c	n

I found _____ words. (List them on another paper.)

SUBTRACTION

Name_____

Use the decoder to find the secret message.

m	d	y	t	a	i	o	e	u
3257	2715	1318	4513	5878	1567	2079	1292	3401

```
   9003          8043          8400          7021
 − 7685        − 5964        − 4999        − 3764
```

```
   6407          6700          3400          7004          5308
 −  529        − 3985        − 2108        − 5437        −  795
```

___ ___ ___ ___ ___ ___ ___ ___ ___ ___ !

Find the End Number.

40
© 1990 Instructional Fair, Inc.

CROSS NUMBER PUZZLE

Name_____

Across
1. 9×2
3. $320 + 8$
6. $48 + 4$
7. $606 \div 3$
8. $50 - 4$
11. $10 + 9$
13. $864 \div 2$
15. 7×6
16. 11×9
17. $3930 \div 10$

Down
1. 5×3
2. $799 + 25$
3. 8×4
4. $618 \div 3$
5. $574 \div 7$
9. $512 + 100$
10. $2196 \div 4$
12. $1353 \div 11$
14. $7 \times 5 + 4$
15. 7×7

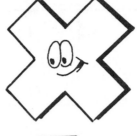

CROSS NUMBER PUZZLE

Name _____

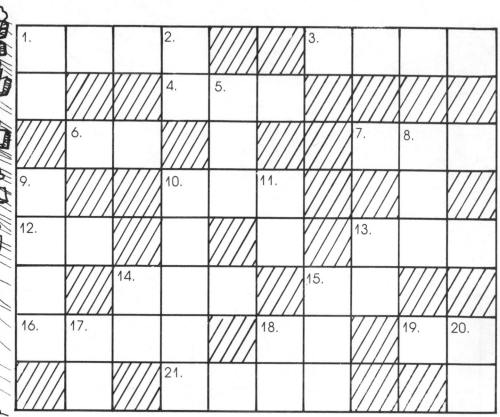

Across

1. 321×6
3. $4010 - 299$
4. 150×3
6. $750 \div 25$
7. $23 + 57 + 62$
10. $8136 \div 9$
12. 9×9
13. $620 - 402$
14. $4218 \div 6$
15. $21 + 62 + 4$
16. 1304×5
18. $69 \div 3$
19. $9 \times 5 + 18$
21. $9593 - 4981$

Down

1. $24 \div 2$
2. 8×8
5. 80×7
8. $819 - 398$
9. $5499 + 2397$
10. 934×106
11. 7×7
13. $9 + 9 + 9$
14. 8×9
15. $1104 - 272$
17. $8 \times 6 + 9$
18. $126 \div 6$
20. $300 \div 10$

Math IF8744

PARTS of a WHOLE

Name_____

Write the fraction for each drawing.

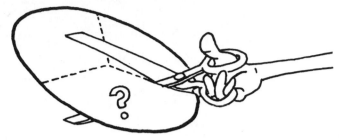

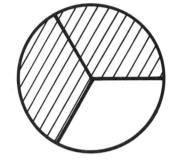 1.

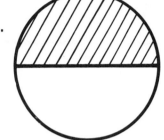 2.

3.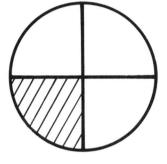

_____

_____

_____

4.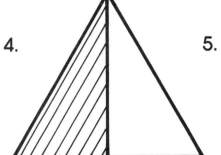

5.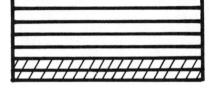

6.

_____

_____

_____

7.

8.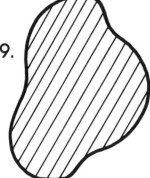

9.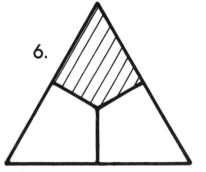

_____

_____

_____

43

FRACTIONS in LOWEST TERMS

Name_____

A fraction is in lowest terms when 1 is the only factor that divides both the numerator and denominator.

    1. Find the greatest common factor.

    2. Divide the numerator and the denominator by their greatest common factor.

$$\frac{8}{16} = \frac{1}{2} \qquad\qquad \frac{18}{24} = \frac{3}{4}$$

1. $\frac{6}{12} =$

2. $\frac{24}{30} =$

3. $\frac{9}{36} =$

4. $\frac{15}{24} =$

5. $\frac{9}{18} =$

6. $\frac{12}{9} =$

7. $\frac{5}{10} =$

8. $\frac{24}{32} =$

9. $\frac{10}{35} =$

10. $\frac{18}{90} =$

11. $\frac{8}{32} =$

12. $\frac{18}{14}$

13. $\frac{2}{6} =$

14. $\frac{12}{18} =$

15. $\frac{24}{9} =$

16. $\frac{7}{28} =$

17. $\frac{6}{21} =$

ADDING FRACTIONS

Name_____

Shade each pie with the fraction.
Then, write the answer.

1. $\frac{1}{2}$ + $\frac{1}{2}$ = _____

2. $\frac{2}{3}$ + $\frac{2}{9}$ = _____

3. $\frac{2}{5}$ + $\frac{1}{3}$ = _____

4. $\frac{1}{2}$ + $\frac{2}{5}$ = _____

5. $\frac{1}{3}$ + $\frac{1}{2}$ = _____

RENAMING IMPROPER and MIXED FRACTIONS

Name_____

To rename $\frac{7}{6}$ as a mixed numeral, do step by step the following.

1. Divide numerator by denominator.
2. Write quotient as a whole number.
3. Write remainder over divisor.
4. Always reduce to lowest terms.

$$\frac{7}{6} \rightarrow 6\overline{)\,7\,}^{1\,R1} = 1\frac{1}{6}$$
$$\frac{-6}{1}$$

1. $\frac{14}{3} =$

2. $\frac{29}{5} =$

3. $\frac{4}{3} =$

4. $\frac{11}{9} =$

5. $\frac{7}{2} =$

6. $\frac{36}{8} =$

7. $\frac{18}{5} =$

8. $\frac{9}{5} =$

To rename $1\frac{1}{2}$ as an improper fraction, study these steps.

1. Multiply the denominator by the whole number.
2. Add the numerator.
3. Write the sum over the denominator.

$$1\frac{1}{2} \rightarrow \frac{(1 \times 2) + 1}{2} = \frac{3}{2}$$

9. $5\frac{7}{10} =$

10. $2\frac{4}{12} =$

11. $5\frac{1}{3} =$

12. $7\frac{5}{8} =$

13. $4\frac{3}{4} =$

14. $2\frac{5}{10} =$

15. $9\frac{1}{7} =$

  46

ADDITION - (Mixed Numerals)

Name_____

$$3\frac{1}{5} = 3\frac{2}{10}$$
$$+ 2\frac{7}{10} = 2\frac{7}{10}$$
$$5\frac{9}{10}$$

$$5\frac{1}{4} = 5\frac{3}{12}$$
$$+ 1\frac{1}{6} = 1\frac{2}{12}$$
$$6\frac{5}{12}$$

1. $8\frac{1}{3}$
    $+ 7\frac{1}{4}$

2. $6\frac{3}{4}$
    $+ 2\frac{1}{8}$

3. $9\frac{7}{10}$
    $+ 8\frac{1}{15}$

4. $8\frac{7}{10}$
    $+ 1\frac{1}{5}$

5. $5\frac{5}{6}$
    $+ 3\frac{1}{12}$

6. $4\frac{1}{2}$
    $+ 7\frac{1}{3}$

7. $5\frac{1}{2}$
    $+ 2\frac{1}{3}$

8. $7\frac{1}{6}$
    $+ 8\frac{1}{4}$

9. $5\frac{1}{3}$
    $+ 3\frac{4}{9}$

10. $6\frac{1}{5}$
     $+ 1\frac{7}{10}$

11. $1\frac{1}{7}$
     $+ 5\frac{3}{7}$

12. $3\frac{1}{2}$
     $+ 4\frac{1}{4}$

Challenge—
Solve the equations.

$$3\frac{7}{8} + 1\frac{3}{4} = 5 + n$$

$$15\frac{3}{8} + 29\frac{5}{6} = 45 + n$$

Math IF8744

47

© 1990 Instructional Fair, Inc.

SUBTRACTING FRACTIONS

Name_____

Example—

$$3\frac{1}{2} = 3\frac{3}{6}$$
$$-2\frac{2}{6} = 2\frac{2}{6}$$
$$\overline{1\frac{1}{6}}$$

$$\frac{1}{2} - \frac{1}{8} - \frac{1}{16} =$$

Subtract. Show all work.

1. $3\frac{4}{7}$
   $-1\frac{1}{14}$

2. $8\frac{5}{6}$
   $-3\frac{3}{8}$

3. $7\frac{7}{8}$
   $-2\frac{1}{4}$

4. $6\frac{1}{2}$
   $-1\frac{5}{12}$

5. $7\frac{3}{8}$
   $-6\frac{1}{6}$

6. $9\frac{1}{2}$
   $-6\frac{1}{12}$

7. $8\frac{2}{3}$
   $-4\frac{1}{6}$

8. $5\frac{1}{2}$
   $-2\frac{1}{4}$

9. $9\frac{4}{5}$
   $-1\frac{3}{10}$

10. $9\frac{2}{5}$
    $-2\frac{4}{15}$

11. $6\frac{7}{12}$
    $-1\frac{1}{2}$

12. $9\frac{1}{3}$
    $-8\frac{1}{4}$

MULTIPLYING a FRACTION
by a FRACTION

Name_____

Find $\frac{3}{4}$ of $\frac{8}{9}$. Cancel where you can.

$$\frac{\overset{1}{\cancel{3}}}{\underset{1}{\cancel{4}}} \times \frac{\overset{2}{\cancel{8}}}{\underset{3}{\cancel{9}}} = \frac{2}{3}$$

Multiply numerators.
Multiply denominators.

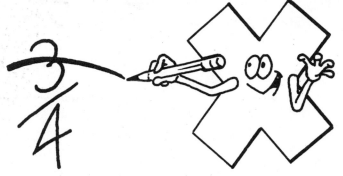

1. $\frac{1}{4} \times \frac{3}{5} =$

2. $\frac{5}{8} \times \frac{3}{10} =$

3. $\frac{3}{8} \times \frac{16}{21} =$

4. $\frac{7}{8} \times \frac{6}{21} =$

5. $\frac{5}{12} \times \frac{8}{15} =$

6. $\frac{8}{9} \times \frac{27}{32} =$

7. $\frac{2}{9} \times \frac{3}{4} =$

8. $\frac{4}{5} \times \frac{25}{36} =$

9. $\frac{7}{8} \times \frac{16}{35} =$

10. $\frac{5}{12} \times \frac{8}{15} =$

11. $\frac{7}{12} \times \frac{9}{28} =$

12. $\frac{6}{7} \times \frac{21}{48} =$

13. $\frac{39}{45} \times \frac{5}{13} =$

14. $\frac{21}{32} \times \frac{16}{35} =$

15. $\frac{8}{11} \times \frac{33}{40} =$

16. $\frac{7}{11} \times \frac{22}{49} =$

17. $\frac{3}{7} \times \frac{21}{24} =$

18. $\frac{5}{9} \times \frac{27}{35} =$

19. $\frac{3}{10} \times \frac{5}{6} =$

20. $\frac{4}{9} \times \frac{27}{32} =$

MULTIPLYING FRACTIONS

Name_____

Multiply the problems in the puzzle.

$7 \times \frac{1}{5}$ $9 \times \frac{1}{10}$ $8 \times \frac{1}{8}$ $8 \times \frac{1}{7}$

$7 \times \frac{1}{11}$ $9 \times \frac{1}{3}$ $3 \times \frac{1}{6}$ $12 \times \frac{1}{5}$

$\frac{1}{5} \times 4$ $\frac{1}{3} \times 9$ $\frac{1}{5} \times 20$ $\frac{1}{6} \times 12$

$\frac{1}{10} \times \frac{1}{100}$ $\frac{1}{6} \times \frac{1}{10}$ $\frac{1}{12} \times \frac{1}{3}$ $\frac{1}{6} \times \frac{1}{6}$

$\frac{1}{9} \times \frac{1}{8}$ $\frac{1}{9} \times \frac{1}{10}$ $\frac{1}{10} \times \frac{1}{10}$ $\frac{1}{20} \times \frac{1}{5}$

$8 \times \frac{1}{10}$ $\frac{1}{5} \times \frac{1}{8}$ $\frac{1}{6} \times \frac{1}{7}$ $\frac{1}{100} \times \frac{1}{100}$

$\frac{1}{9} \times 9$ $\frac{1}{8} \times 7$ $\frac{1}{7} \times 6$ $12 \times \frac{1}{4}$

$\frac{1}{15} \times \frac{1}{13}$ $\frac{1}{3} \times \frac{1}{7}$ $\frac{1}{8} \times 3$ $\frac{1}{7} \times 21$

ADDING LIKE FRACTIONS

Name_____

Add problems to find the real gem. Shade in answer gems. The one left is the real gem.

$$\frac{3}{8} + \frac{2}{8}$$ 　　$$\frac{4}{7} + \frac{1}{7}$$ 　　$$\frac{4}{6} + \frac{1}{6}$$ 　　$$\frac{1}{3} + \frac{1}{3}$$ 　　$$\frac{1}{4} + \frac{1}{4}$$ 　　$$\frac{1}{8} + \frac{1}{8}$$ 　　$$\frac{1}{6} + \frac{2}{6}$$

$$\frac{1}{8} + \frac{4}{8}$$ 　　$$\frac{3}{20} + \frac{4}{20}$$ 　　$$\frac{4}{10} + \frac{3}{10}$$ 　　$$\frac{1}{5} + \frac{3}{5}$$ 　　$$\frac{4}{12} + \frac{5}{12}$$ 　　$$\frac{5}{15} + \frac{4}{15}$$ 　　$$\frac{14}{20} + \frac{5}{20}$$

$$\frac{3}{16} + \frac{5}{16}$$ 　　$$\frac{1}{8} + \frac{6}{8}$$ 　　$$\frac{2}{5} + \frac{1}{5}$$ 　　$$\frac{7}{12} + \frac{2}{12}$$ 　　$$\frac{2}{13} + \frac{5}{13}$$ 　　$$\frac{5}{17} + \frac{8}{17}$$ 　　$$\frac{9}{18} + \frac{8}{18}$$

$$\frac{3}{15} + \frac{5}{15}$$ 　　$$\frac{5}{12} + \frac{2}{12}$$ 　　$$\frac{5}{14} + \frac{4}{14}$$ 　　$$\frac{1}{7} + \frac{5}{7}$$ 　　$$\frac{6}{16} + \frac{7}{16}$$ 　　$$\frac{7}{21} + \frac{8}{21}$$ 　　$$\frac{5}{10} + \frac{4}{10}$$

Math IF8744

51

© 1990 Instructional Fair, Inc.

ADDING 3 FRACTIONS

Name_____

Work problems. Shade in answers on balloon **A** or **B** height to see how high each balloon flew.

$\frac{1}{10}$ $\frac{4}{10}$ $+\frac{3}{10}$	$\frac{1}{5}$ $\frac{2}{5}$ $+\frac{1}{5}$	$\frac{1}{7}$ $\frac{1}{7}$ $+\frac{1}{7}$	$\frac{4}{9}$ $\frac{1}{9}$ $+\frac{2}{9}$
$\frac{1}{4}$ $\frac{1}{4}$ $+\frac{1}{4}$	$\frac{1}{10}$ $\frac{7}{10}$ $+\frac{1}{10}$	$\frac{3}{7}$ $\frac{2}{7}$ $+\frac{1}{7}$	$\frac{2}{8}$ $\frac{1}{8}$ $+\frac{2}{8}$
$\frac{3}{9}$ $\frac{3}{9}$ $+\frac{2}{9}$	$\frac{5}{15}$ $\frac{3}{15}$ $+\frac{4}{15}$	$\frac{1}{10}$ $\frac{5}{10}$ $+\frac{1}{10}$	$\frac{5}{11}$ $\frac{1}{11}$ $+\frac{4}{11}$
$\frac{3}{12}$ $\frac{5}{12}$ $+\frac{1}{12}$	$\frac{4}{7}$ $\frac{1}{7}$ $+\frac{1}{7}$	$\frac{7}{14}$ $\frac{2}{14}$ $+\frac{4}{14}$	$\frac{6}{20}$ $\frac{7}{20}$ $+\frac{4}{20}$
$\frac{3}{8}$ $\frac{2}{8}$ $+\frac{1}{8}$	$\frac{9}{21}$ $\frac{5}{21}$ $+\frac{4}{21}$	$\frac{2}{13}$ $\frac{1}{13}$ $+\frac{7}{13}$	$\frac{7}{16}$ $\frac{3}{16}$ $+\frac{5}{16}$

A	B
$\frac{3}{8}$	$\frac{14}{15}$
$\frac{8}{11}$	$\frac{11}{14}$
$\frac{19}{21}$	$\frac{13}{16}$
$\frac{13}{15}$	$\frac{9}{13}$
$\frac{5}{7}$	$\frac{9}{11}$
$\frac{6}{9}$	$\frac{11}{15}$
$\frac{3}{5}$	$\frac{7}{8}$
$\frac{15}{16}$	$\frac{4}{7}$
$\frac{9}{10}$	$\frac{2}{4}$
$\frac{10}{13}$	$\frac{3}{4}$
$\frac{8}{10}$	$\frac{17}{20}$
$\frac{10}{11}$	$\frac{5}{8}$
$\frac{13}{14}$	$\frac{7}{10}$
$\frac{8}{9}$	$\frac{12}{15}$
$\frac{6}{8}$	$\frac{18}{21}$
$\frac{3}{7}$	$\frac{4}{5}$
$\frac{9}{12}$	$\frac{6}{7}$
$\frac{6}{7}$	$\frac{7}{9}$

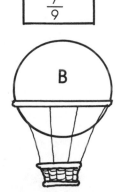

Which balloon flew the highest?

FRACTIONS: LOWEST TERMS

$\frac{6}{20}$	largest number that will divide evenly into both $$\frac{6}{20} \div \frac{2}{2} = \frac{3}{10}$$	$\frac{6}{20} = \frac{3}{10}$

Reduce to lowest terms.

$\frac{5}{20} = \frac{}{4}$ $\qquad$ $\frac{8}{20} = \underline{}$ $\qquad$ $\frac{3}{15} = \underline{}$ $\qquad$ $\frac{12}{20} = \underline{}$

$\frac{2}{8} = \underline{}$ $\qquad$ $\frac{12}{16} = \underline{}$ $\qquad$ $\frac{14}{16} = \underline{}$ $\qquad$ $\frac{4}{8} = \underline{}$

$\frac{9}{12} = \underline{}$ $\qquad$ $\frac{5}{10} = \underline{}$ $\qquad$ $\frac{6}{10} = \underline{}$ $\qquad$ $\frac{10}{15} = \underline{}$

$\frac{2}{4} = \underline{}$ $\qquad$ $\frac{4}{8} = \underline{}$ $\qquad$ $\frac{6}{24} = \underline{}$ $\qquad$ $\frac{6}{8} = \underline{}$

$\frac{8}{16} = \underline{}$ $\qquad$ $\frac{2}{12} = \underline{}$ $\qquad$ $\frac{2}{10} = \underline{}$ $\qquad$ $\frac{8}{12} = \underline{}$

$\frac{4}{20} = \underline{}$ $\qquad$ $\frac{3}{12} = \underline{}$ $\qquad$ $\frac{9}{15} = \underline{}$ $\qquad$ $\frac{4}{12} = \underline{}$

$\frac{10}{24} = \underline{}$ $\qquad$ $\frac{6}{20} = \underline{}$ $\qquad$ $\frac{10}{12} = \underline{}$ $\qquad$ $\frac{12}{24} = \underline{}$

$\frac{4}{10} = \underline{}$ $\qquad$ $\frac{8}{10} = \underline{}$ $\qquad$ $\frac{2}{10} = \underline{}$ $\qquad$ $\frac{6}{12} = \underline{}$

EQUIVALENT FRACTIONS

Name_____

Match the pairs of equivalent fractions.

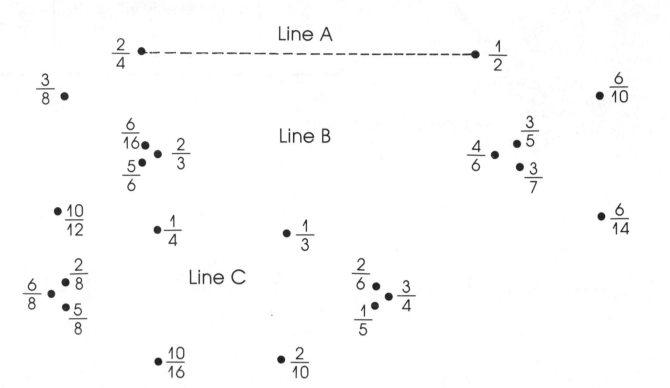

Which line is longer? **A**, **B** or **C**.

$\frac{2}{3}$

Line B

$\frac{2}{6}$
$\frac{2}{16}$
Line A
$\frac{3}{4}$
$\frac{1}{3}$ $\frac{1}{2}$

$\frac{5}{8}$ $\frac{3}{8}$

$\frac{10}{16}$ $\frac{6}{16}$
$\frac{9}{12}$ $\frac{1}{8}$
$\frac{3}{12}$
Line C

$\frac{1}{4}$ $\frac{5}{10}$

$\frac{4}{6}$

Which line is longer? **A**, **B** or **C**.

© 1990 Instructional Fair, Inc.

FRACTIONS: IMPROPER TO MIXED   Name _____

Change fractions to mixed numbers. Shade in each answer to find the path to the pot of gold.

1. $\frac{11}{9}$ =

2. $\frac{8}{3}$ =

3. $\frac{8}{7}$ =

4. $\frac{11}{6}$ =

5. $\frac{7}{3}$ =

6. $\frac{7}{6}$ =

7. $\frac{9}{4}$ =

8. $\frac{8}{5}$ =

9. $\frac{4}{3}$ =

10. $\frac{7}{2}$ =

11. $\frac{3}{2}$ =

12. $\frac{6}{5}$ =

13. $\frac{7}{4}$ =

14. $\frac{9}{2}$ =

15. $\frac{11}{8}$ =

16. $\frac{5}{2}$ =

17. $\frac{9}{7}$ =

18. $\frac{11}{4}$ =

19. $\frac{17}{12}$ =

20. $\frac{13}{12}$ =

Row 1: $1\frac{3}{5}$ $1\frac{1}{12}$ $2\frac{3}{4}$ $1\frac{4}{7}$ $2\frac{1}{6}$ $1\frac{5}{7}$ $1\frac{3}{8}$

Row 2: $1\frac{11}{12}$ $4\frac{1}{3}$ $1\frac{1}{2}$ $1\frac{4}{5}$ $3\frac{3}{4}$ $4\frac{3}{4}$ $2\frac{1}{4}$ $2\frac{5}{6}$ $2\frac{6}{7}$

Row 3: $4\frac{1}{2}$ $3\frac{1}{3}$ $2\frac{1}{2}$ $1\frac{7}{12}$ $1\frac{5}{8}$ $2\frac{1}{3}$ $3\frac{1}{2}$ $1\frac{1}{5}$ $1\frac{6}{7}$

Row 4: $1\frac{2}{9}$ $2\frac{1}{5}$ $1\frac{5}{12}$ $1\frac{3}{4}$ $1\frac{1}{3}$ $1\frac{5}{6}$ $3\frac{1}{6}$ $4\frac{2}{3}$ $2\frac{4}{5}$

Row 5: $1\frac{1}{7}$ $1\frac{4}{9}$ $1\frac{2}{3}$ $1\frac{3}{7}$ $1\frac{1}{6}$ $2\frac{2}{3}$ $1\frac{2}{7}$

FRACTIONS: MIXED TO IMPROPER

Name_____

Work problems. Connect dots in the order of the answers

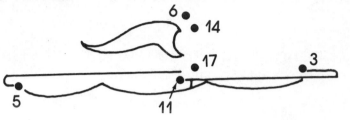

1. $1\frac{2}{5} = \frac{}{5}$

2. $1\frac{1}{3} = \frac{}{3}$

3. $1\frac{5}{7} = \frac{}{7}$

4. $2\frac{2}{3} = \frac{}{3}$

5. $2\frac{5}{8} = \frac{}{8}$

6. $2\frac{1}{2} = \frac{}{2}$

7. $1\frac{5}{6} = \frac{}{6}$

8. $1\frac{1}{5} = \frac{}{5}$

9. $2\frac{4}{5} = \frac{}{5}$

10. $1\frac{1}{16} = \frac{}{16}$

11. $1\frac{1}{2} = \frac{}{2}$

12. $3\frac{1}{5} = \frac{}{5}$

13. $1\frac{11}{12} = \frac{}{12}$

14. $1\frac{7}{8} = \frac{}{8}$

15. $1\frac{6}{7} = \frac{}{7}$

16. $2\frac{1}{4} = \frac{}{4}$

17. $1\frac{7}{12} = \frac{}{12}$

18. $1\frac{3}{7} = \frac{}{7}$

19. $6\frac{2}{3} = \frac{}{3}$

20. $3\frac{3}{5} = \frac{}{5}$

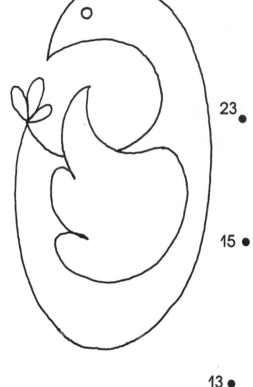

21. $1\frac{5}{21} = \frac{}{21}$

22. $1\frac{7}{36} = \frac{}{36}$

23. $1\frac{9}{20} = \frac{}{20}$

24. $1\frac{13}{24} = \frac{}{24}$

© 1990 Instructional Fair, Inc.

ADDING UNLIKE FRACTIONS

Name_____

Work problems. Shade in answers on pizzas to show which pieces have been eaten.

$\frac{1}{10}$
$+\frac{4}{5}$
_____

$\frac{3}{12}$
$+\frac{1}{6}$
_____

$\frac{1}{2}$
$+\frac{1}{3}$
_____

$\frac{3}{4}$
$+\frac{1}{5}$
_____

$\frac{1}{5}$
$+\frac{1}{3}$
_____

$\frac{2}{3}$
$+\frac{1}{4}$
_____

$\frac{5}{12}$
$+\frac{1}{6}$
_____

$\frac{2}{5}$
$+\frac{9}{20}$
_____

$\frac{1}{3}$
$+\frac{2}{9}$
_____

$\frac{3}{5}$
$+\frac{1}{10}$
_____

$\frac{1}{4}$
$+\frac{1}{2}$
_____

$\frac{1}{8}$
$+\frac{1}{4}$
_____

$\frac{1}{10}$
$+\frac{1}{5}$
_____

$\frac{2}{3}$
$+\frac{1}{5}$
_____

$\frac{1}{8}$
$+\frac{1}{3}$
_____

$\frac{1}{4}$
$+\frac{1}{5}$
_____

$\frac{3}{8}$
$+\frac{1}{5}$
_____

$\frac{9}{16}$
$+\frac{3}{8}$
_____

$\frac{2}{8}$
$+\frac{9}{16}$
_____

$\frac{1}{5}$
$+\frac{1}{9}$
_____

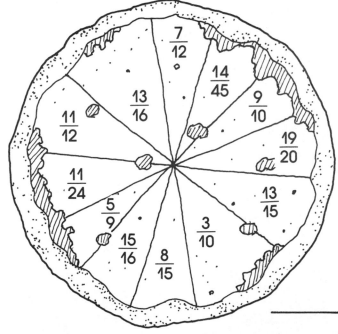

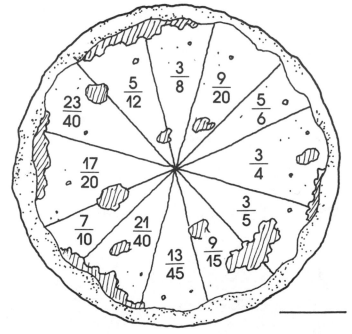

Which fractional part of each pizza has been eaten?

ADDING UNLIKE FRACTIONS

Name_____

Work problems. Use answers to guide coloring of stained glass window. Reduce fractions to lowest terms.

red
$$52\frac{4}{9}$$
$$+ \ 8\frac{7}{8}$$

blue
$$16\frac{2}{7}$$
$$+ 14\frac{1}{3}$$

green
$$40\frac{1}{2}$$
$$+ 50\frac{2}{3}$$

orange
$$36\frac{5}{6}$$
$$+ 57\frac{1}{2}$$

blue
$$39\frac{3}{4}$$
$$+ 54\frac{5}{8}$$

red
$$72\frac{3}{4}$$
$$+ 67\frac{5}{8}$$

yellow
$$84\frac{5}{6}$$
$$+ 94\frac{2}{3}$$

orange
$$35\frac{7}{8}$$
$$+ 36\frac{1}{2}$$

purple
$$4\frac{3}{8}$$
$$+ \ 3\frac{3}{4}$$

orange
$$7\frac{3}{4}$$
$$+ \ 8\frac{3}{8}$$

green
$$8\frac{1}{2}$$
$$+ \ 3\frac{5}{8}$$

yellow
$$6\frac{5}{6}$$
$$+ \ 4\frac{1}{2}$$

red
$$3\frac{3}{4}$$
$$+ \ 4\frac{3}{5}$$

orange
$$5\frac{1}{2}$$
$$+ \ 6\frac{3}{4}$$

green
$$9\frac{11}{15}$$
$$+ \ 4\frac{7}{10}$$

purple
$$4\frac{3}{5}$$
$$+ \ 2\frac{3}{5}$$

purple
$$4\frac{5}{12}$$
$$+ \ 2\frac{5}{6}$$

purple
$$4\frac{5}{6}$$
$$+ \ 3\frac{1}{3}$$

red
$$5\frac{1}{3}$$
$$+ \ 7\frac{9}{10}$$

blue
$$37\frac{5}{7}$$
$$+ 46\frac{7}{9}$$

green
$$33\frac{7}{8}$$
$$+ 19\frac{11}{12}$$

blue
$$4\frac{4}{7}$$
$$+ \ 5\frac{5}{6}$$

Name_____

Work problems. Where you find an answer, put an **X**.
Where you don't, put an **O**.

$\frac{3}{4}$	$\frac{8}{12}$	$\frac{2}{5}$
$\frac{2}{3}$	$\frac{1}{12}$	$\frac{10}{12}$
$\frac{7}{8}$	$\frac{7}{10}$	$\frac{11}{11}$

$$1\frac{1}{9} - \frac{7}{9} = \frac{3}{9}$$

$$1\frac{1}{4} - \frac{3}{4}$$

$$1\frac{1}{8} - \frac{5}{8}$$

$$1\frac{2}{5} - \frac{4}{5}$$

$$1\frac{1}{3} - \frac{2}{3}$$

$$1\frac{1}{12} - \frac{5}{12}$$

$$1\frac{1}{7} - \frac{6}{7}$$

$$1\frac{3}{5} - \frac{4}{5}$$

$\times$ (3/8)	$\frac{5}{7}$	$\frac{4}{10}$
$\frac{11}{15}$	$\frac{31}{40}$	$\frac{5}{8}$
$\frac{9}{12}$	$\frac{11}{24}$	$\frac{2}{7}$

$$1\frac{1}{6} - \frac{5}{6}$$

$$1\frac{3}{8} - \frac{7}{8}$$

$$1\frac{5}{12} - \frac{7}{12}$$

$$1\frac{1}{12} - \frac{1}{3}$$

$$1\frac{1}{8} - \frac{1}{2}$$

$$1\frac{1}{8} - \frac{3}{4}$$

$$1\frac{5}{8} - \frac{3}{4}$$

$$1\frac{1}{10} - \frac{1}{2}$$

$\frac{3}{8}$	$\frac{3}{10}$	$\frac{2}{4}$
$\frac{3}{5}$	$\frac{17}{20}$	$\frac{4}{8}$
$\frac{2}{6}$	$\frac{4}{5}$	$\frac{14}{15}$

$$1\frac{1}{5} - \frac{1}{4}$$

$$1\frac{1}{8} - \frac{2}{3}$$

$$1\frac{1}{2} - \frac{3}{4}$$

$$1\frac{1}{3} - \frac{6}{7}$$

$$1\frac{1}{5} - \frac{3}{8}$$

$$1\frac{4}{5} - \frac{9}{10}$$

$\frac{6}{7}$	$\frac{10}{21}$	$\frac{8}{15}$
$\frac{13}{20}$	$\frac{13}{24}$	$\frac{7}{19}$
$\frac{17}{24}$	$\frac{33}{40}$	$\frac{3}{13}$

$\frac{4}{8}$	$\frac{5}{12}$	$\frac{3}{7}$
$\frac{9}{10}$	$\frac{5}{20}$	$\frac{5}{10}$
$\frac{29}{40}$	$\frac{19}{20}$	$\frac{6}{10}$

$$1\frac{1}{4} - \frac{3}{5}$$

$$1\frac{1}{3} - \frac{4}{5}$$

SUBTRACTING UNLIKE FRACTIONS Name_____

Work problems to solve riddle. Cross out answers to find out what letters are left.

$$\begin{array}{r} \frac{1}{2} \\ -\frac{1}{5} \\ \hline \end{array}$$
$$\begin{array}{r} \frac{1}{3} \\ -\frac{1}{4} \\ \hline \end{array}$$
$$\begin{array}{r} \frac{1}{3} \\ -\frac{1}{6} \\ \hline \end{array}$$
$$\begin{array}{r} \frac{2}{3} \\ -\frac{2}{5} \\ \hline \end{array}$$
$$\begin{array}{r} \frac{5}{9} \\ -\frac{1}{2} \\ \hline \end{array}$$

$$\begin{array}{r} \frac{2}{3} \\ -\frac{1}{2} \\ \hline \end{array}$$
$$\begin{array}{r} \frac{5}{6} \\ -\frac{1}{5} \\ \hline \end{array}$$
$$\begin{array}{r} \frac{4}{5} \\ -\frac{5}{10} \\ \hline \end{array}$$
$$\begin{array}{r} \frac{3}{4} \\ -\frac{1}{3} \\ \hline \end{array}$$
$$\begin{array}{r} \frac{1}{3} \\ -\frac{1}{5} \\ \hline \end{array}$$

$$\begin{array}{r} \frac{4}{5} \\ -\frac{1}{4} \\ \hline \end{array}$$
$$\begin{array}{r} \frac{11}{12} \\ -\frac{1}{3} \\ \hline \end{array}$$
$$\begin{array}{r} \frac{3}{4} \\ -\frac{2}{5} \\ \hline \end{array}$$
$$\begin{array}{r} \frac{1}{3} \\ -\frac{2}{9} \\ \hline \end{array}$$
$$\begin{array}{r} \frac{7}{8} \\ -\frac{1}{4} \\ \hline \end{array}$$

$$\begin{array}{r} \frac{5}{8} \\ -\frac{1}{2} \\ \hline \end{array}$$
$$\begin{array}{r} \frac{11}{16} \\ -\frac{4}{16} \\ \hline \end{array}$$
$$\begin{array}{r} \frac{5}{6} \\ -\frac{4}{5} \\ \hline \end{array}$$
$$\begin{array}{r} \frac{13}{18} \\ -\frac{4}{9} \\ \hline \end{array}$$
$$\begin{array}{r} \frac{9}{14} \\ -\frac{2}{7} \\ \hline \end{array}$$

What did the turkey say at Thanksgiving? _____

B $\frac{3}{10}$	E $\frac{2}{12}$	J $\frac{1}{6}$	A $\frac{4}{18}$	O $\frac{2}{15}$	T $\frac{7}{18}$	F $\frac{1}{18}$
P $\frac{11}{20}$	U $\frac{3}{10}$	C $\frac{9}{16}$	T $\frac{4}{15}$	H $\frac{4}{30}$	N $\frac{5}{18}$	E $\frac{13}{20}$
G $\frac{1}{9}$	E $\frac{3}{8}$	M $\frac{7}{20}$	D $\frac{5}{14}$	K $\frac{7}{12}$	S $\frac{7}{16}$	W $\frac{1}{30}$
H $\frac{5}{12}$	I $\frac{1}{6}$	X $\frac{19}{30}$	S $\frac{5}{9}$	L $\frac{1}{12}$	R $\frac{5}{8}$	E $\frac{3}{7}$	V $\frac{1}{8}$

SUBTRACTING UNLIKE FRACTIONS   Name_____

Work problems.
Use answers to decode and say GREAT in . . .

 French

Chinese

$$\overline{\quad}\ \overline{\quad}\ \overline{\quad}\ \overline{\quad}\ \quad\ \overline{\quad}\ \overline{\quad}\ \overline{\quad}$$
$$2\frac{9}{10}\quad 4\frac{3}{8}\quad 4\frac{9}{20}\quad 1\frac{5}{8}\qquad 28\frac{7}{9}\quad 1\frac{1}{2}\quad 9\frac{3}{8}$$

$$\overline{\quad}\ \overline{\quad}\ \overline{\quad}\ \overline{\quad}$$
$$1\frac{7}{10}\quad 1\frac{29}{40}\quad 4\frac{5}{6}\quad 9\frac{19}{70}$$

$$\overline{\quad}\ \overline{\quad}\ \overline{\quad}\ \overline{\quad}$$
$$17\frac{9}{16}\quad 41\frac{37}{56}\quad 2\frac{3}{4}\quad 3\frac{13}{15}$$

$$\overline{\quad}\ \overline{\quad}\ \overline{\quad}\qquad \overline{\quad}\ \overline{\quad}\ \overline{\quad}\ \overline{\quad}\ \overline{\quad}\ \overline{\quad}\ \overline{\quad}$$
$$2\frac{7}{8}\quad 5\frac{7}{12}\quad 4\frac{3}{4}\qquad 1\frac{15}{16}\ 7\frac{3}{5}\ 3\frac{7}{12}\ 11\frac{1}{2}\ 3\frac{3}{4}\ 35\frac{25}{28}\ 4\frac{15}{28}$$

Japanese

S. $21\frac{7}{10}$ $-12\frac{3}{7}$

H. $76\frac{4}{9}$ $-47\frac{2}{3}$

D. $5\frac{1}{5}$ $-2\frac{3}{10}$

A. $4\frac{1}{8}$ $-2\frac{3}{16}$

W. $10\frac{1}{8}$ $-\frac{3}{4}$

L. $59\frac{3}{4}$ $-23\frac{6}{7}$

S. $12\frac{1}{3}$ $-\frac{5}{6}$

E. $6\frac{2}{3}$ $-1\frac{5}{6}$

I. $5\frac{1}{4}$ $-\frac{7}{8}$

N. $7\frac{2}{3}$ $-3\frac{4}{5}$

N. $16\frac{7}{10}$ $-12\frac{1}{4}$

R. $8\frac{3}{5}$ $-6\frac{7}{8}$

G. $3\frac{1}{2}$ $-1\frac{7}{8}$

L. $7\frac{2}{7}$ $-2\frac{3}{4}$

H. $6\frac{1}{2}$ $-2\frac{3}{4}$

B. $71\frac{5}{16}$ $-53\frac{3}{4}$

S. $7\frac{1}{4}$ $-4\frac{3}{8}$

A. $5\frac{1}{4}$ $-1\frac{2}{3}$

E. $7\frac{1}{4}$ $-4\frac{1}{2}$

B. $12\frac{1}{2}$ $-7\frac{3}{4}$

I. $83\frac{2}{7}$ $-41\frac{5}{8}$

O. $8\frac{1}{3}$ $-6\frac{5}{6}$

T. $7\frac{3}{10}$ $-5\frac{3}{5}$

U. $14\frac{1}{3}$ $-8\frac{3}{4}$

R. $16\frac{1}{10}$ $-8\frac{1}{2}$

EQUIVALENT FRACTIONS

Name_____

Connect the equivalent fractions to complete the picture.

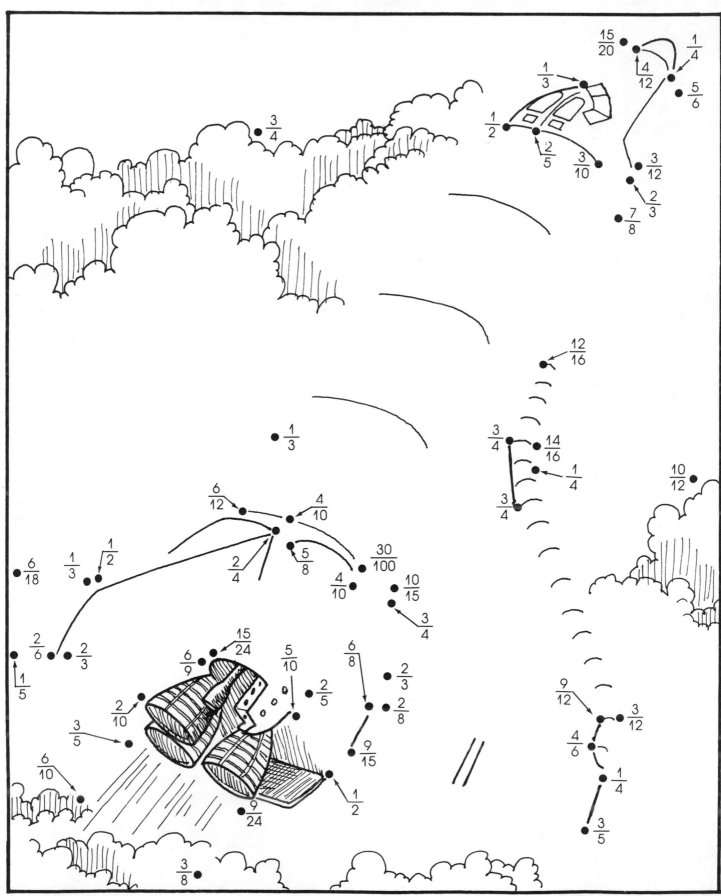

FRACTION REVIEW: + −

Name_____

Work each problem. Write
answer in square.

a. $\frac{1}{4} + \frac{1}{6} =$ e. $\frac{1}{3} + \frac{1}{6} =$

b. $\frac{1}{2} + \frac{1}{3} =$ f. $\frac{1}{6} + \frac{1}{2} =$

c. $\frac{1}{2} - \frac{1}{4} =$ g. $\frac{5}{6} - \frac{1}{12} =$

d. $\frac{1}{2} - \frac{1}{6} =$ h. $\frac{1}{2} - \frac{1}{3} =$

i. $\frac{1}{4} + \frac{1}{3} =$

Add every row, every column and
both diagonals. If your answers are
correct, all totals will be the same.

a.	b.	c.
d.	e.	f.
g.	h.	i.

_____

_____

_____

_____ _____ _____ _____

Complete the table.

+	$\frac{1}{8}$	$\frac{1}{3}$			
$\frac{1}{4}$			$\frac{5}{12}$	$\frac{7}{8}$	$\frac{9}{20}$
$\frac{1}{5}$					
			$\frac{1}{2}$		
				$\frac{3}{4}$	
			$\frac{1}{3}$		

Complete these tables.

+	$\frac{1}{2}$	$\frac{1}{3}$	$\frac{1}{4}$	$\frac{1}{5}$	$\frac{1}{6}$
$\frac{1}{8}$					

+	$\frac{1}{2}$	$\frac{1}{3}$	$\frac{1}{4}$	$\frac{1}{5}$	$\frac{1}{6}$
$\frac{1}{12}$					

FRACTION REVIEW

Name_____

Reduce to lowest terms. Shade each part that is equivalent to $\frac{1}{2}$, $\frac{1}{3}$ or $\frac{3}{4}$.

What travels in all directions, yet is neither in the air nor on the ground?

_____

$\frac{4}{6}$	$\frac{10}{15}$	$\frac{6}{15}$	$\frac{2}{20}$	$\frac{4}{10}$

$\frac{5}{20}$ $\frac{8}{12}$ $\frac{4}{32}$ $\frac{18}{24}$ $\frac{14}{20}$

$\frac{12}{15}$ $\frac{12}{20}$ $\frac{6}{20}$

$\frac{3}{12}$ $\frac{6}{10}$ $\frac{6}{12}$ $\frac{4}{12}$ $\frac{18}{20}$ $\frac{4}{14}$

$\frac{10}{12}$ $\frac{16}{28}$

$\frac{8}{32}$ $\frac{2}{16}$ $\frac{6}{24}$

$\frac{8}{20}$ $\frac{4}{10}$ $\frac{10}{18}$

$\frac{2}{12}$ $\frac{3}{15}$ $\frac{14}{18}$

$\frac{9}{27}$ $\frac{3}{9}$ $\frac{6}{18}$ $\frac{9}{21}$

$\frac{3}{6}$ $\frac{2}{10}$ $\frac{5}{10}$

$\frac{14}{16}$ $\frac{12}{16}$ $\frac{4}{20}$ $\frac{3}{12}$ $\frac{4}{8}$ $\frac{8}{10}$

$\frac{6}{8}$ $\frac{9}{12}$

$\frac{6}{20}$

$\frac{9}{15}$ $\frac{2}{4}$ $\frac{2}{6}$ $\frac{5}{15}$ $\frac{15}{20}$

$\frac{6}{9}$

$\frac{4}{18}$ $\frac{10}{24}$ $\frac{25}{35}$

Math IF8744   64   © 1990 Instructional Fair, Inc.

MULTIPLYING FRACTIONS

Name_____

Work problems. Use code to color the design: **B**-blue, **Y**-yellow, **O**-orange, **G**-green.

$\frac{5}{6} \times \frac{3}{4} =$ ___ B $\frac{7}{10} \times \frac{3}{5} =$ ___ Y $\frac{2}{3} \times \frac{7}{8} =$ ___ G $\frac{3}{4} \times \frac{3}{5} =$ ___ O

$\frac{5}{6} \times \frac{4}{5} =$ ___ Y $\frac{3}{8} \times \frac{8}{10} =$ ___ Y $\frac{9}{16} \times \frac{5}{6} =$ ___ O $\frac{4}{7} \times \frac{1}{6} =$ ___ G

$\frac{5}{9} \times \frac{3}{5} =$ ___ Y $\frac{7}{12} \times \frac{5}{6} =$ ___ B $\frac{2}{5} \times \frac{1}{3} =$ ___ B $\frac{9}{10} \times \frac{2}{3} =$ ___ Y

$\frac{5}{8} \times \frac{3}{5} =$ ___ B $\frac{1}{3} \times \frac{4}{5} =$ ___ Y $\frac{3}{4} \times \frac{5}{8} =$ ___ O $\frac{5}{6} \times \frac{3}{8} =$ ___ B

$\frac{2}{5} \times \frac{5}{8} =$ ___ Y $\frac{5}{6} \times \frac{1}{3} =$ ___ O $\frac{7}{9} \times \frac{1}{4} =$ ___ O $\frac{3}{8} \times \frac{5}{12} =$ ___ O

$\frac{3}{7} \times \frac{14}{15} =$ ___ G $\frac{3}{4} \times \frac{2}{3} =$ ___ B $\frac{2}{7} \times \frac{3}{7} =$ ___ G $\frac{5}{6} \times \frac{1}{10} =$ ___ Y

$\frac{2}{3} \times \frac{4}{5} =$ ___ O $\frac{7}{10} \times \frac{5}{8} =$ ___ O $\frac{1}{6} \times \frac{5}{6} =$ ___ B $\frac{3}{4} \times \frac{4}{5} =$ ___ B

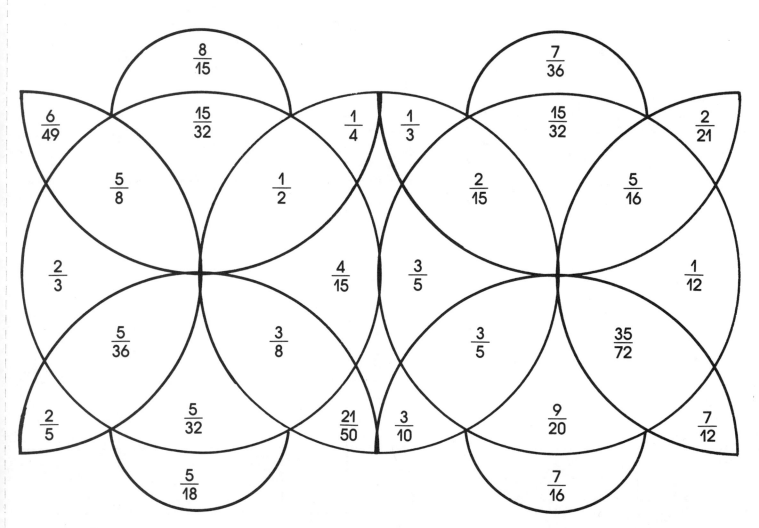

MULTIPLYING FRACTIONS

Name_____

Complete these tables.

X	$\frac{3}{5}$	$\frac{1}{2}$	$\frac{2}{3}$	$\frac{1}{6}$	$\frac{1}{8}$
$\frac{1}{2}$	$\frac{3}{10}$				
$\frac{3}{8}$					
$\frac{4}{7}$					
$\frac{5}{8}$					
$\frac{1}{10}$					

X	$\frac{1}{2}$	$\frac{3}{4}$	$\frac{1}{6}$	$\frac{3}{8}$	$\frac{1}{3}$
$\frac{1}{4}$					
$\frac{1}{8}$					
$\frac{1}{5}$					
$\frac{2}{7}$					
$\frac{1}{3}$					

MULTIPLYING with MIXED NUMBERS

Name_____

Change mixed numbers to improper fractions before multiplying.

$$300 \times 3\frac{1}{4}$$

$$\frac{\overset{75}{\cancel{300}}}{1} \times \frac{13}{\cancel{4}_{1}} = \frac{975}{1} = 975$$

1. $5\frac{1}{4} \times 3\frac{1}{5}$

2. $2\frac{1}{3} \times 2\frac{1}{4}$

3. $1\frac{1}{9} \times 3\frac{3}{5}$

4. $2\frac{5}{8} \times 5\frac{1}{3}$

5. $2\frac{6}{7} \times 5\frac{1}{4}$

6. $3\frac{3}{4} \times 1\frac{3}{5}$

7. $3\frac{2}{3} \times 2\frac{1}{7}$

8. $4\frac{1}{6} \times 3\frac{3}{5}$

9. $6\frac{2}{5} \times 3\frac{1}{8}$

10. $1\frac{1}{7} \times 2\frac{5}{8}$

11. $6\frac{3}{8} \times 1\frac{1}{9}$

12. $3\frac{3}{4} \times \frac{2}{3}$

13. $1\frac{1}{9} \times \frac{3}{4}$

14. $3\frac{3}{8} \times 5\frac{1}{3}$

15. $5\frac{1}{3} \times \frac{9}{20}$

16. $2\frac{1}{4} \times \frac{4}{9}$

MULTIPLYING FRACTIONS

Name_____

Work problems. Find answer and circle letter. Write letters in order for message.

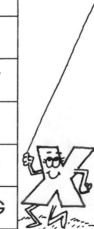

Problem		
$2\frac{2}{3} \times \frac{3}{4} =$	$2\frac{1}{4}$ A	2 S
$4\frac{2}{3} \times 5\frac{1}{4} =$	$24\frac{1}{3}$ B	$24\frac{1}{2}$ U
$3\frac{3}{4} \times 5\frac{7}{9} =$	$21\frac{2}{3}$ P	$21\frac{1}{3}$ C
$6\frac{2}{5} \times 2\frac{1}{2} =$	$15\frac{1}{2}$ D	16 E
$5\frac{1}{5} \times 3\frac{1}{2} =$	$18\frac{1}{5}$ R	$18\frac{2}{5}$ F
$3\frac{1}{2} \times 3\frac{3}{4} =$	$13\frac{1}{8}$ N	$13\frac{3}{8}$ H
$5\frac{5}{9} \times 5\frac{1}{4} =$	$29\frac{5}{6}$ G	$29\frac{1}{6}$ O
$4\frac{5}{8} \times 2\frac{4}{5} =$	$12\frac{19}{20}$ W	$12\frac{17}{20}$ J
$5\frac{4}{7} \times 4\frac{1}{5} =$	$23\frac{1}{5}$ I	$23\frac{2}{5}$ Y
$5\frac{3}{4} \times \frac{4}{5} =$	$4\frac{3}{5}$ O	$4\frac{1}{5}$ L
$3\frac{3}{4} \times 2\frac{1}{6} =$	$8\frac{3}{8}$ K	$8\frac{1}{8}$ U
$5\frac{2}{3} \times 7\frac{4}{5} =$	$44\frac{2}{5}$ M	$44\frac{1}{5}$ '
$4\frac{1}{2} \times 2\frac{5}{8} =$	$11\frac{13}{16}$ R	$11\frac{11}{16}$ O
$3\frac{3}{5} \times 4\frac{3}{8} =$	$15\frac{3}{4}$ E	$15\frac{1}{4}$ R
$6\frac{5}{9} \times 3\frac{3}{5} =$	$23\frac{3}{5}$ F	$23\frac{1}{5}$ U
$2\frac{2}{3} \times 5\frac{13}{16} =$	$15\frac{1}{3}$ N	$15\frac{1}{2}$ L
$3\frac{1}{7} \times 2\frac{5}{12} =$	$7\frac{23}{42}$ Q	$7\frac{25}{42}$ Y
$4\frac{4}{5} \times 3\frac{3}{4} =$	18 I	17 T
$2\frac{1}{3} \times 3\frac{3}{4} =$	$8\frac{3}{4}$ N	$8\frac{1}{3}$ P
$3\frac{1}{3} \times 2\frac{3}{4} =$	$9\frac{5}{6}$ S	$9\frac{1}{6}$ G

_ _ _ _ _ _ !

_ _ _

_ _ _ _ _ _

_ _ _ _ _ _ _ !

MULTIPLYING FRACTIONS

Multiply. Reduce to lowest terms.

Name_____

1. $2\frac{2}{3} \times 3\frac{1}{4} =$

2. $3\frac{7}{9} \times 1\frac{7}{8} =$

3. $4\frac{2}{8} \times 5\frac{3}{5} =$

4. $4\frac{1}{3} \times 7\frac{1}{2} =$

5. $5\frac{3}{8} \times 4\frac{3}{4} =$

6. $\frac{6}{7} \times 5\frac{2}{8} =$

7. $5 \times \frac{20}{100} =$

8. $3\frac{1}{5} \times 2\frac{1}{8} =$

9. $\frac{4}{7} \times \frac{14}{20} =$

10. $9\frac{3}{4} \times 5\frac{1}{3} =$

11. $2\frac{1}{2} \times 1\frac{1}{3} =$

12. $4 \times 2\frac{1}{3} =$

13. $2\frac{3}{4} \times 5\frac{1}{3} =$

14. $1\frac{9}{10} \times 1\frac{1}{4} =$

15. $3\frac{4}{8} \times 5\frac{3}{7} =$

16. $6\frac{1}{4} \times 3\frac{2}{5} =$

17. $5\frac{3}{5} \times 2\frac{6}{7} =$

18. $5\frac{5}{8} \times 4\frac{2}{9} =$

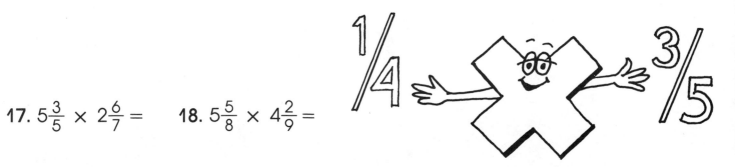

69

DIVIDING FRACTIONS

Name_____

$$6 \div \frac{1}{4}$$

$$\frac{6}{1} \div \frac{1}{4} \qquad \text{Step - 1}$$

$$\frac{6}{1} \times \frac{4}{1} \qquad \text{Step - 2}$$

$$\frac{24}{1} \qquad \text{Step - 3}$$

$$24 \qquad \text{Step - 4}$$

1. $7 \div \frac{1}{3}$

2. $8 \div \frac{1}{2}$

3. $16 \div \frac{1}{3}$

4. $6 \div \frac{1}{2}$

5. $5 \div \frac{1}{6}$

6. $18 \div \frac{1}{7}$

7. $8 \div \frac{1}{5}$

8. $7 \div \frac{1}{9}$

9. $15 \div \frac{1}{6}$

DIVIDING FRACTIONS

Name_____

In division of fractions:
1. Change the sign " ÷ " to " × ".
2. Invert the divisor.
3. Cancel where possible.
4. Multiply numerators.
5. Multiply denominators.
6. If quotient is an improper fraction, change to a mixed number.

Show all work. Cancel where you can.

1. $18 \div 2\frac{1}{4}$

2. $52 \div 2\frac{8}{9}$

3. $8 \div 5\frac{1}{3}$

4. $39 \div 2\frac{1}{2}$

5. $50 \div 3\frac{1}{8}$

6. $45 \div 3\frac{3}{4}$

7. $63 \div 2\frac{5}{8}$

8. $42 \div 4\frac{1}{5}$

9. $25 \div 1\frac{1}{9}$

DIVIDING FRACTIONS

Name_____

Work each problem below. Color the shape if the answer is a whole number.

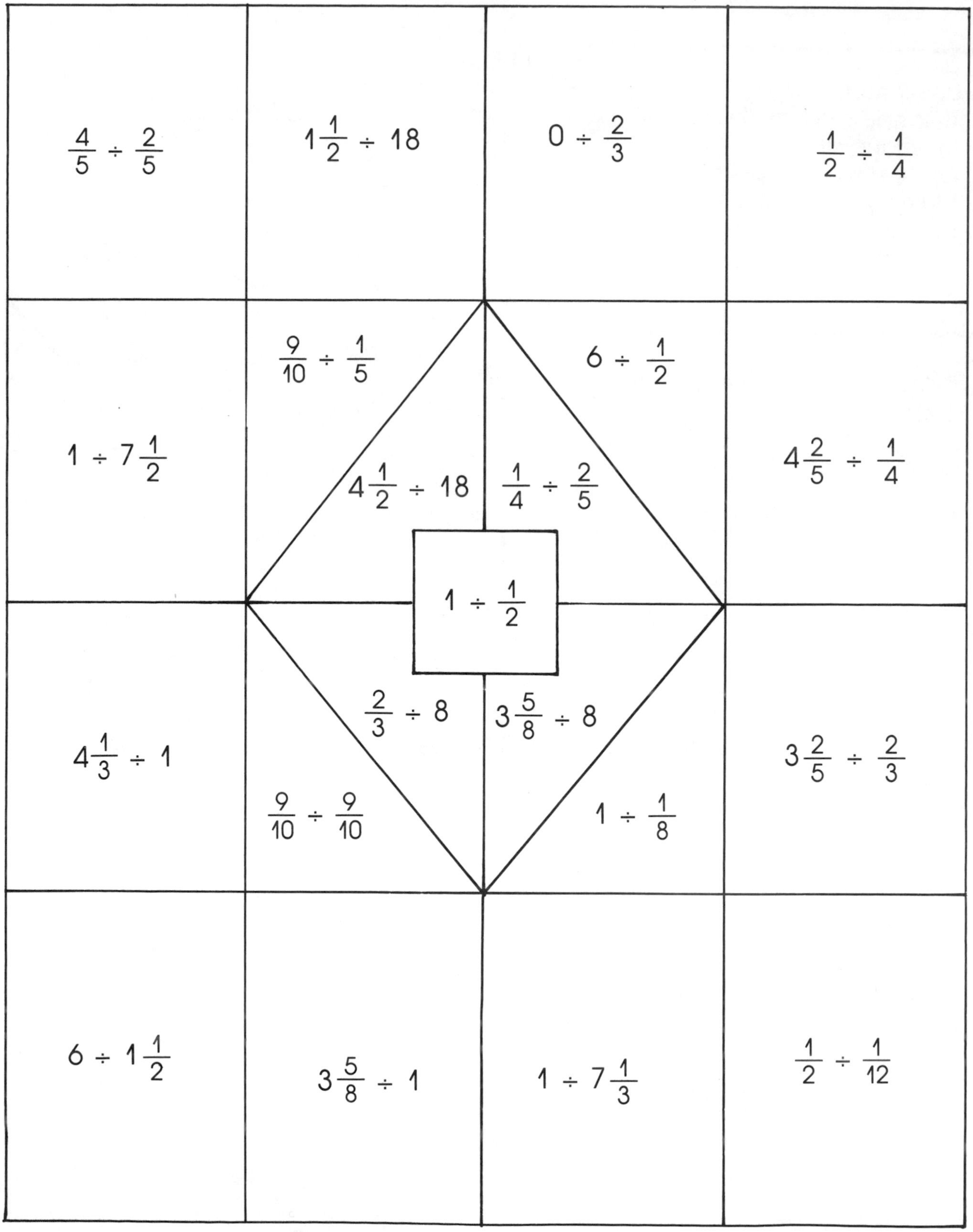

$\frac{4}{5} \div \frac{2}{5}$	$1\frac{1}{2} \div 18$	$0 \div \frac{2}{3}$	$\frac{1}{2} \div \frac{1}{4}$
$1 \div 7\frac{1}{2}$	$\frac{9}{10} \div \frac{1}{5}$ $4\frac{1}{2} \div 18$ $\frac{1}{4} \div \frac{2}{5}$	$6 \div \frac{1}{2}$ $1 \div \frac{1}{2}$	$4\frac{2}{5} \div \frac{1}{4}$
$4\frac{1}{3} \div 1$	$\frac{9}{10} \div \frac{9}{10}$ $\frac{2}{3} \div 8$ $3\frac{5}{8} \div 8$	$1 \div \frac{1}{8}$	$3\frac{2}{5} \div \frac{2}{3}$
$6 \div 1\frac{1}{2}$	$3\frac{5}{8} \div 1$	$1 \div 7\frac{1}{3}$	$\frac{1}{2} \div \frac{1}{12}$

DIVIDING FRACTIONS

Name_____

Work problems. Arrange your work this way:

$$6 \div \frac{1}{4} = \frac{6}{1} \div \frac{1}{4} = \frac{6}{1} \times \frac{4}{1} = \frac{24}{1} = \textbf{24}$$

$7 \div \frac{1}{3} =$	$8 \div \frac{1}{2} =$
$16 \div \frac{1}{3} =$	$6 \div \frac{1}{2} =$
$5 \div \frac{1}{6} =$	$18 \div \frac{1}{7} =$
$8 \div \frac{1}{5} =$	$7 \div \frac{1}{9} =$
$15 \div \frac{1}{6} =$	$2\frac{1}{2} \div \frac{1}{2} =$
$3\frac{1}{9} \div \frac{1}{3} =$	$5\frac{1}{4} \div \frac{3}{8} =$

The smallest answer is _____. The largest answer is _____.

DIVIDING FRACTIONS

Name_____

Reduce to lowest terms.

1. $\frac{1}{5} \div 3$

2. $\frac{5}{7} \div 15$

3. $\frac{7}{8} \div 21$

4. $\frac{3}{5} \div 12$

5. $\frac{3}{7} \div 6$

6. $\frac{3}{8} \div 6$

7. $\frac{5}{7} \div 10$

8. $\frac{5}{6} \div 15$

9. $\frac{7}{10} \div 2$

10. $\frac{7}{8} \div 14$

11. $\frac{7}{9} \div 7$

12. $\frac{1}{4} \div 3$

13. $\frac{8}{9} \div 16$

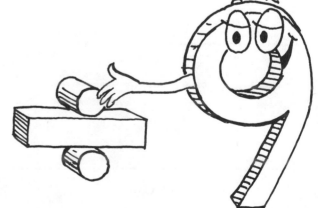

PARTS of a SET

Name_____

Write a fraction to answer each question.

1.  What part of this set of plants is a flower? _____

2.  What part of this set of drawings are squares? _____

3. What part of this set of containers is full? _____

4. What part of this set of animals are cats? _____

5. What part of this set of eggs are broken? _____

Challenge:

6. What part of your class are boys? _____ girls? _____

7. How many dollars in $\$\frac{18}{6}$? _____ In $\$\frac{30}{6}$? _____

8. How many 6ths in 1? _____

9. How many hours in $\frac{5}{12}$ of a day? _____ In $\frac{7}{12}$ of a day? _____

10. How many things in $\frac{11}{12}$ of a dozen? _____

☆ Write five questions like the above ones on another sheet of paper.

NUMBER CHALLENGE

Work each problem, starting at the top
of each machine, working down.

Name_____

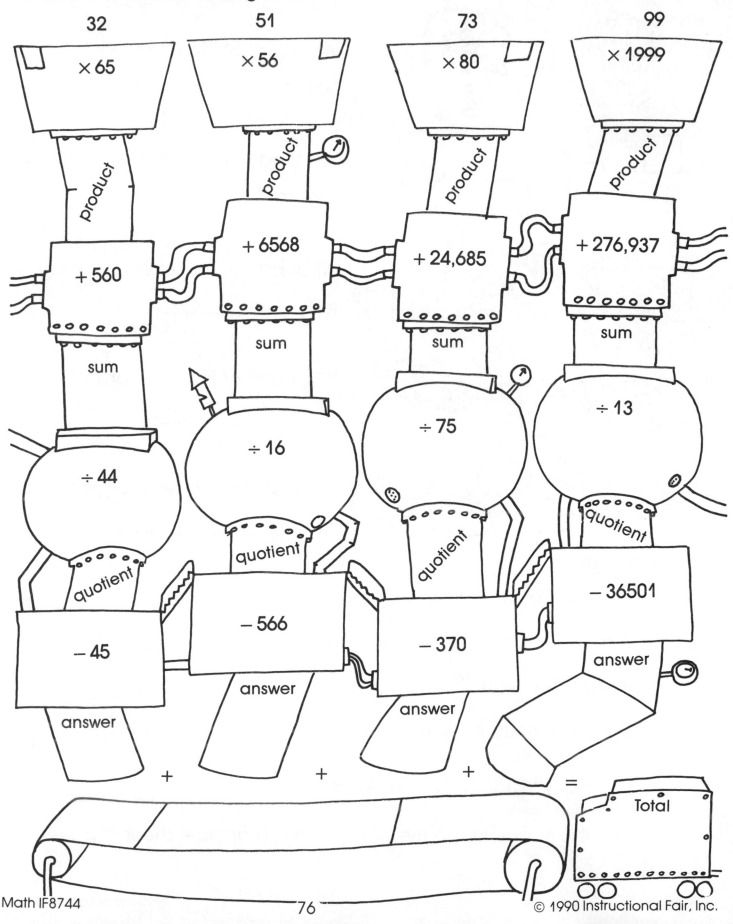

32
×65

51
×56

73
×80

99
×1999

product

product

product

product

+560

+6568

+24,685

+276,937

sum

sum

sum

sum

÷44

÷16

÷75

÷13

quotient

quotient

quotient

quotient

−45

−566

−370

−36501

answer

answer

answer

answer

+   +   +   =

Total

WRITING DECIMALS

Name_____

Decimals are names for fractional numbers. Write each fraction as a decimal.

1. $\frac{7}{10}$ = _____

2. $\frac{2}{10}$ = _____

3. $\frac{78}{100}$ = _____

4. $38\frac{1}{10}$ = _____

5. $3\frac{2}{100}$ = _____

6. $4\frac{36}{100}$ = _____

7. $\frac{3}{10}$ = _____

8. $\frac{4}{100}$ = _____

9. $\frac{21}{1000}$ = _____

10. $8\frac{103}{1000}$ = _____

11. $7\frac{16}{100}$ = _____

12. $1\frac{8}{10}$ = _____

13. $\frac{2}{10}$ = _____

14. $14\frac{8}{10}$ = _____

15. $38\frac{1}{10}$ = _____

16. $\frac{6}{10}$ = _____

17. $7\frac{6}{10}$ = _____

18. $\frac{3}{10}$ = _____

19. $15\frac{6}{10}$ = _____

20. $\frac{4}{10}$ = _____

21. $\frac{1}{4}$ = _____

22. $\frac{3}{8}$ = _____

23. $\frac{5}{8}$ = _____

24. $\frac{1}{40}$ = _____

25. $\frac{200}{400}$ = _____

26. $\frac{50}{125}$ = _____

27. $\frac{7}{8}$ = _____

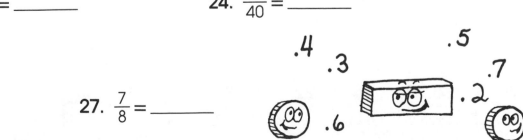

.4 .3 .5 .7 .2 .6

ADDITION of DECIMALS

Name_____

Add and check work. Keep columns straight.

1. .5
   + .7

2. 2.5
   + 3.8

3. 47.6
   + 32.9

4. 85.6
   + 9.7

5. .34
   + .25

6. 3.91
   + 4.23

7. 9.43
   + 8.16

8. 72.9
   + 83.4

9. 6.34
   + 4.57

10. 24.39
    + 8.70

11. 1.9
    + .7

12. 343.8
    +   9.6

13. 638.072
    +   9.340

14. 921.063
    + 72.430

15. 821.03
    + 40.76

16. 726.435
    + 814.291

17. 72.413
    + 18.943

18. 63.987
    + 72.431

19. 814.2
    + 72.6

20. 981.1
    +   1.3

21. 926.723
    + 72.631

22. 87.876
    + 63.591

ADDING DECIMALS

Name_____

Add problems.

| hops | .3 | | .5 | .4 | .7 | .3 | .7 | .4 | |
| hops | .2 | | .9 | .7 | .8 | .8 | .3 | .8 | |

| jumps | 2.3 | | 9.8 | 2.6 | 3.7 | 4.3 | 3.5 | 7.7 | |
| jumps | 1.3 | | | 2.7 | 9.6 | 8.9 | 4.8 | |

| steps | 9.33 | | 6.231 | 24.8 | 1.1 | 16.2 | 7.893 | 23.7 | |
| steps | 14.865 | | | 8.9 | 3.8 | 2.5 | 6.005 | |

| flaps | 15.01 | | .002 | 14.003 | 4.27 | 1.002 | .219 | .02 | |
| flaps | 26.305 | | | 6.16 | 35.213 | 3.152 | 27.106 | |

| leaps | 1.6 | | 5.82 | 11.7 | 3.9 | 15.0 | 3.98 | 4.5 | |
| leaps | 8.91 | | | 8.1 | 3.76 | 7.88 | 5.3 | 14.7 | |

| beep-beeps | | 738.8 | 27.4 | 753.547 | 139.62 | | 37.2 | |
| beep-beeps | | 4.8 | 43.96 | 6.73 | 15.227 | 2.683 | | |

© 1990 Instructional Fair, Inc.

ADDING DECIMALS

Name_____

Add center number to number in first circle to find the answer. Next, add all answers on wheel. Then, add all wheel answers to get total of all wheels.

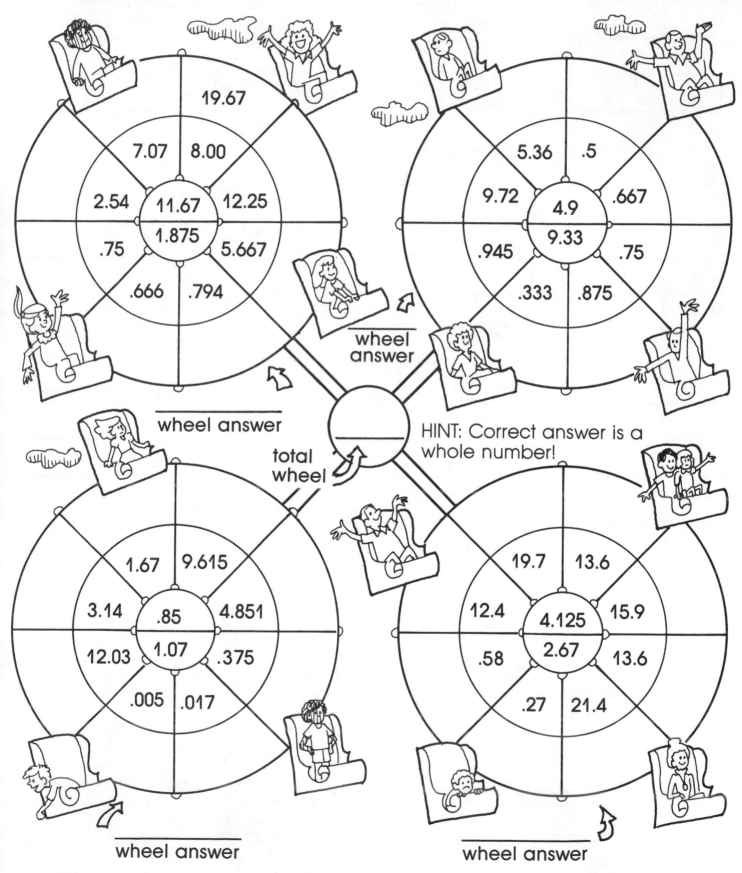

19.67

7.07 8.00

2.54 **11.67** 12.25
      1.875
.75   5.667

.666 .794

wheel answer

wheel answer

total wheel

5.36 .5

9.72 **4.9** .667
      9.33
.945   .75

.333 .875

wheel answer

HINT: Correct answer is a whole number!

1.67 9.615

3.14 **.85** 4.851
      1.07
12.03   .375

.005 .017

wheel answer

19.7 13.6

12.4 **4.125** 15.9
      2.67
.58   13.6

.27 21.4

wheel answer

ADDING DECIMALS

Name_____

Arrange the six numbers above each triangle so that each arm adds up to the number shown in the box in the center.

4.32
2.21, 3.25, 3.28, 4.51, 3.47

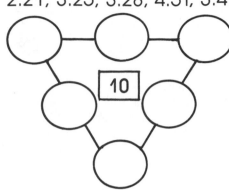

4.3, 4.4, 5.8, 2.9, 7.8, 6.3

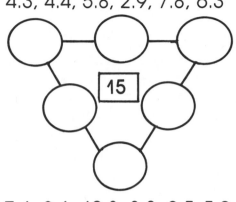

3.3, 3.2, 3.5, 4.5, 4.3, 2.2

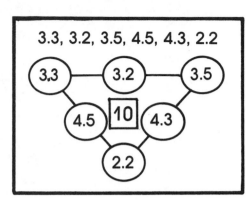

6.9, 8.6, 7.8, 4.5, 7.7, 3.6

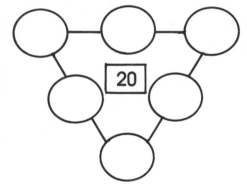

7.1, 9.6, 10.8, 8.3, 9.5, 5.9

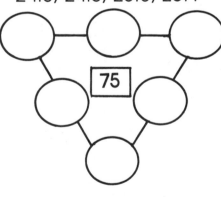

17.52, 15.72,
17.33, 15.15, 16.95, 16.76

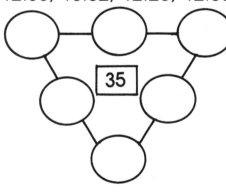

33.34, 33.36,
33.33, 33.35, 33.31, 33.3,

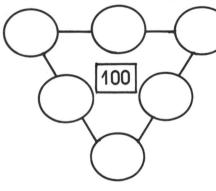

24.9, 25.6,
24.3, 24.5, 25.8, 25.1

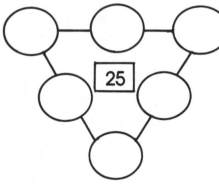

12.57, 10.4,
12.35, 10.62, 12.25, 12.03

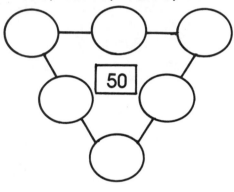

13.67, 13.63
12.92, 13.41, 13.45, 13.14

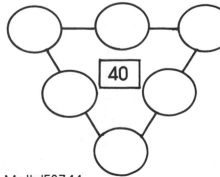

14.23, 15.73,
15.24, 15.44, 14.03, 15.53

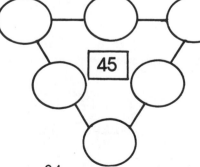

167.82, 167.38, 167.42,
166.11, 166.07, 166.51

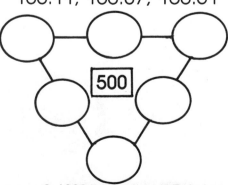

SUBTRACTION of DECIMALS

Name_____

Subtract. Check all problems.

1. 2.4
   − .6

2. .79
   − .08

3. 18.24
   − 7.56

4. 38.57
   − 16.83

5. 1.9
   − .7

6. 13.5
   − 7.3

7. 29.6
   − 19.8

8. 42.6
   − 8.1

9. 98.21
   − 6.43

10. 2.7
   − .7

11. 48.9
   − 9.8

12. 63.29
   − 9.43

13. 6.34
   − 4.57

14. 12.6
   − 6.5

15. 93.21
   − 9.43

16. 691.98
   − 42.69

17. 4.26
   − .02

18. 98.6
   − 7.8

19. 26.43
   − 1.49

20. 987.23
   − 8.97

21. 7.2
   − 6.7

22. 88.7
   − 43.8

23. 95.7
   − 8.6

24. 143.29
   − 86.74

SUBTRACTING DECIMALS

Name_____

Work problems. Use answers to name the kittens. Match names with answers.
One is left for you to name.

					Harvey 1.283

$$\begin{array}{r} 6.815 \\ -3.968 \\ \hline 2.847 \end{array} \qquad \begin{array}{r} 6.405 \\ -3.283 \\ \hline \end{array} \qquad \begin{array}{r} 6.300 \\ -1.138 \\ \hline \end{array} \qquad \begin{array}{r} 4.182 \\ -3.295 \\ \hline \end{array} \qquad \begin{array}{r} 16.200 \\ -7.893 \\ \hline \end{array}$$

Felix				

$$\begin{array}{r} 3.105 \\ -\ .246 \\ \hline \end{array} \qquad \begin{array}{r} 1.589 \\ -\ .306 \\ \hline \end{array} \qquad \begin{array}{r} 9.200 \\ -3.032 \\ \hline \end{array} \qquad \begin{array}{r} 9.305 \\ -6.283 \\ \hline \end{array} \qquad \begin{array}{r} 8.263 \\ -3.352 \\ \hline \end{array}$$

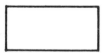 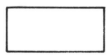   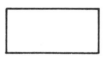 

$$\begin{array}{r} 117.52 \\ -\ 74.25 \\ \hline \end{array} \qquad \begin{array}{r} 6.895 \\ -4.174 \\ \hline \end{array} \qquad \begin{array}{r} 8.975 \\ -1.017 \\ \hline \end{array} \qquad \begin{array}{r} 16.206 \\ -\ 5.359 \\ \hline \end{array} \qquad \begin{array}{r} 17.001 \\ -\ 9.09 \\ \hline \end{array}$$

$$\begin{array}{r} 8.495 \\ -3.653 \\ \hline \end{array} \qquad \begin{array}{r} 9.975 \\ -7.781 \\ \hline \end{array} \qquad \begin{array}{r} 12.730 \\ -\ 5.283 \\ \hline \end{array} \qquad \begin{array}{r} 17.90 \\ -14.23 \\ \hline \end{array} \qquad \begin{array}{r} 18.152 \\ -11.69 \\ \hline \end{array}$$

  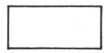

Name list:

Harvey 1.283
Puff 7.958
Ralph 5.162
Tom 3.022
Felix 2.847
Grover 43.27
Smokey .887
Tinker 3.122
Cleo 10.847
Morris 7.447
Kat 2.721
Sunshine 6.462
Sam 2.194
Oscar 7.911
Angel 3.67
Rocky 4.842
Button 6.168
Coco 2.859
Kitti 4.911

SUBTRACTING DECIMALS

Name_____

Work problems. The fisherman can only keep the larger fish, those with answers larger than 7.0. Put the problem number of the fish in the fisherman's basket.

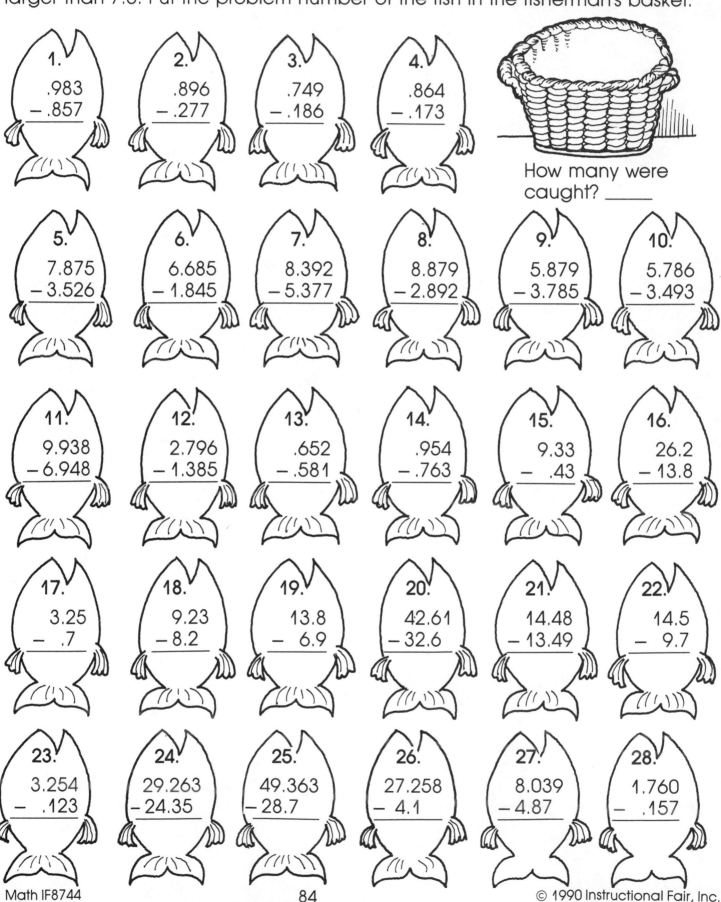

1.
.983
− .857

2.
.896
− .277

3.
.749
− .186

4.
.864
− .173

How many were caught? _____

5.
7.875
− 3.526

6.
6.685
− 1.845

7.
8.392
− 5.377

8.
8.879
− 2.892

9.
5.879
− 3.785

10.
5.786
− 3.493

11.
9.938
− 6.948

12.
2.796
− 1.385

13.
.652
− .581

14.
.954
− .763

15.
9.33
− .43

16.
26.2
− 13.8

17.
3.25
− .7

18.
9.23
− 8.2

19.
13.8
− 6.9

20.
42.61
− 32.6

21.
14.48
− 13.49

22.
14.5
− 9.7

23.
3.254
− .123

24.
29.263
− 24.35

25.
49.363
− 28.7

26.
27.258
− 4.1

27.
8.039
− 4.87

28.
1.760
− .157

84

MULTIPLYING DECIMALS

Name_____

Work problems. Find answer and circle letter. Write letters in order for message.

Problem		Choice 1		Choice 2		Choice 3	
4.98 × 100	=	4.98	B	498	W	49.8	H
2.6 × 10	=	26	H	26.	I	2.6	C
7.2 × 100	=	.72	I	720	A	7.2	
.64 × 100	=	.64	P	6.4	G	64	T
.432 × 1000	=	432	A	4.32	W	43.2	G
53 × 10	=	530	M	5.3	F	.53	X
4.7 × 10	=	.47	V	47	A	470	F
3.1 × 100	=	310	R	3100	B	.31	O
100 × .02	=	.2	E	.002	C	2	V
100 × 4.82	=	48.2	T	.482	U	482	E
49.9 × 100	=	4.99	N	4990	L	.499	A
.0037 × 100	=	3.7	D	.37	O	.037	Z
.375 × 1000	=	3.75	J	37.5	S	375	U
1000 × .0036	=	3.6	S	.036	Y	.0036	X
6.005 × 1000	=	60.05	H	6005	E	600.5	C
29.5 × 1000	=	29,500	F	2.95	K	.0295	L
100 × .003	=	3.	K	.3	F	.03	P
.372 × 100	=	3.72	E	.0372	Q	37.2	O
10 × 74.3	=	743	R	7.43	S	.743	V
9.67 × 100	=	.967	D	96.7	J	967	T

_ _ _ _   _ _ _ _ _ _ _   _ _   _ _ _ _ _ _ _!

MULTIPLYING DECIMALS

Name_____

Work problems. Where you find an answer, put an **X**.
Where you don't, put an **O**.

4.968	26.88	.3822
1.120	49.68	42.63
9.52	38.22	14.56

$$\begin{array}{r} 4.9 \\ \times\ .87 \\ \hline 343 \\ 3920 \\ \hline 4.263 \end{array}$$

$$\begin{array}{r} 52 \\ \times\ 2.8 \\ \hline \end{array}$$

$$\begin{array}{r} 5.4 \\ \times\ 7.3 \\ \hline \end{array}$$

$$\begin{array}{r} .17 \\ \times\ 5.6 \\ \hline \end{array}$$

$$\begin{array}{r} .49 \\ \times\ .78 \\ \hline \end{array}$$

$$\begin{array}{r} .40 \\ \times\ 2.8 \\ \hline \end{array}$$

$$\begin{array}{r} 9.1 \\ \times\ .18 \\ \hline \end{array}$$

$$\begin{array}{r} 7.7 \\ \times\ 37 \\ \hline \end{array}$$

11.12	.0870	267.88
28.49	2.064	1.638
⊠ 4.263	8.75	3.942

$$\begin{array}{r} 8.6 \\ \times\ 2.4 \\ \hline \end{array}$$

$$\begin{array}{r} 2.5 \\ \times\ 3.5 \\ \hline \end{array}$$

$$\begin{array}{r} 54 \\ \times\ .92 \\ \hline \end{array}$$

$$\begin{array}{r} .62 \\ \times\ 83 \\ \hline \end{array}$$

$$\begin{array}{r} .47 \\ \times\ .96 \\ \hline \end{array}$$

$$\begin{array}{r} 9.5 \\ \times\ .74 \\ \hline \end{array}$$

$$\begin{array}{r} .58 \\ \times\ .15 \\ \hline \end{array}$$

$$\begin{array}{r} 5.6 \\ \times\ 4.8 \\ \hline \end{array}$$

20.64	496.8	41.616
514.6	16.38	.4512
.870	145.6	.48051

$$\begin{array}{r} .867 \\ \times\ 48 \\ \hline \end{array}$$

$$\begin{array}{r} 90.6 \\ \times\ .24 \\ \hline \end{array}$$

$$\begin{array}{r} 3.72 \\ \times\ 2.9 \\ \hline \end{array}$$

$$\begin{array}{r} 44.5 \\ \times\ 6.1 \\ \hline \end{array}$$

$$\begin{array}{r} .843 \\ \times\ .57 \\ \hline \end{array}$$

$$\begin{array}{r} 72.4 \\ \times\ 3.7 \\ \hline \end{array}$$

27.145	8.75	.952
70.3	51.46	48.051
217.44	416.16	10.788

How many games did
each win?

X _____ O _____

7.030	2.688	107.88
45.12	21.744	284.9
39.42	26.788	271.45

MULTIPLYING DECIMALS

Name_____

Work problems. Use answers to
guide coloring of design.

green	blue	red
.463	28.5	6.51
× 82	× 7.4	× 6.9

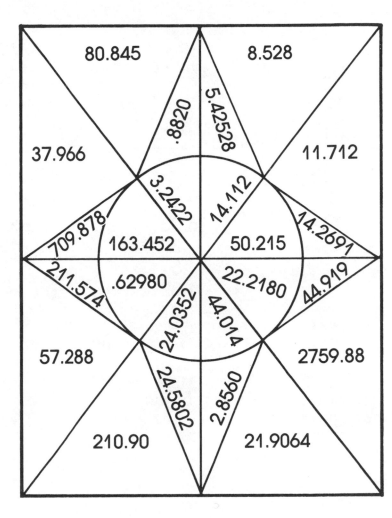

yellow	purple	purple
39.2	7.54	.670
× .36	× .43	× .94

yellow	yellow	purple
64.9	.592	7.46
× 3.26	× 40.6	× 5.9

green	blue	blue	green	purple	green	blue
92.4	32.8	85.1	7.32	6.05	3.27	5.56
× .62	× .26	× .95	× 1.6	× 8.3	× 844	× 3.94

yellow	red	red	red	yellow	yellow	yellow	yellow
80.5	5.77	95.8	.784	2.57	29.3	6.80	.245
× .276	× 4.26	× 7.41	× 6.92	× 63.6	× .487	× .42	× 3.6

DECIMAL REVIEW

Name_____

Work problems. Shade in each answer to find the path to the bug.

.43	35.1	377.5	4.289	13.190
.06	475.11	× 1.53	× 67.3	− 5.734
.28	.54			
.77	.3			
+ 1.01	+ 1.5			

.4392	5.03	.8627	5.621	3.108
×.216	.371	× .456	× 4.87	× .539
	.51			
	1.22			
	+ 1.3			

10.3500	5.764	8.879	3.6	13.066
− 2.3844	+ .49	− 2.933	+ 6.938	− 4.214

25.5 .948672 74.56 28.86497 2.55 27.37427 10.538

8.431 577.575 .0948672 16.75212 288.6497 57.7575 .3933912

6.254 .8431 7.456 51.255 512.55 273.7427 8.852

.03933912 7.9656 1.675212 5.946 79.656

DIVIDING BY A DECIMAL

Name_____

Work problems. Unscramble the letters to find the secret message.

M
$2.1\overline{)8.4}$ = $21.\overline{)84.}$

A
$0.36\overline{)1.872}$

S
$1.24\overline{)0.4712}$

R
$8\overline{)1.12}$

R
$0.3\overline{)17.7}$

L
$6\overline{)126.}$

A
$.80\overline{)16.00}$

E
$6.1\overline{)32.33}$

A
$0.3\overline{)0.234}$

E
$.082\overline{)0.3772}$

H
$0.2\overline{)6.34}$

C
$9\overline{)81.9}$

D
$7.4\overline{)103.6}$

D
$.87\overline{).5307}$

I
$5.5\overline{)3.025}$

D _ _ _ _ _ _ _

_ _ _ _ H _ _ _ !

89

WRITING DECIMALS AS PERCENTS

Name_____

To write a decimal as a percent, move the decimal two places to the right and add a % sign.

.95 _____   .02 _____

7.21 _____   2.5 _____

.08 _____   .156 _____

3.25 _____   .05 _____

.6 _____   .09 _____

.1576 _____   .88 _____

9.25 _____   42.5 _____

.4 _____   9.21 _____

.12 _____   .8 _____

1.90 _____   .42 _____

.240 _____   1.00 _____

.60 _____   .63 _____

.03 _____   1.21 _____

.56 _____   .9 _____

.609 _____   1.5 _____

Rewrite the percentages in order, from smallest to largest._____

_____

_____

_____

BAR GRAPHS

Name _____

1. The bar graph below shows the number of problems each of five pupils had correct in a science test. Fill in each blank with the correct answer.

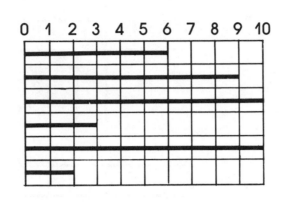

Fill in each blank:

Christy _____   Anthony _____   John _____

Joseph _____   Latriece _____   Mary _____

2. Show the weight of each boy in the sixth grade. Each square represents 10 pounds.

		0	10	20	30	40	50	60	70	80	90	100
Joshua	60 lb.											
Michael	80 lb.											
Danny	70 lb.											
Mark	90 lb.											
Timothy	100 lb.											

3. **Challenge:**
Make a bar graph showing your spelling test grades from last quarter.

100%

MATH WORD PUZZLE

Name_____

Use clues to complete crossword.

Down.

1.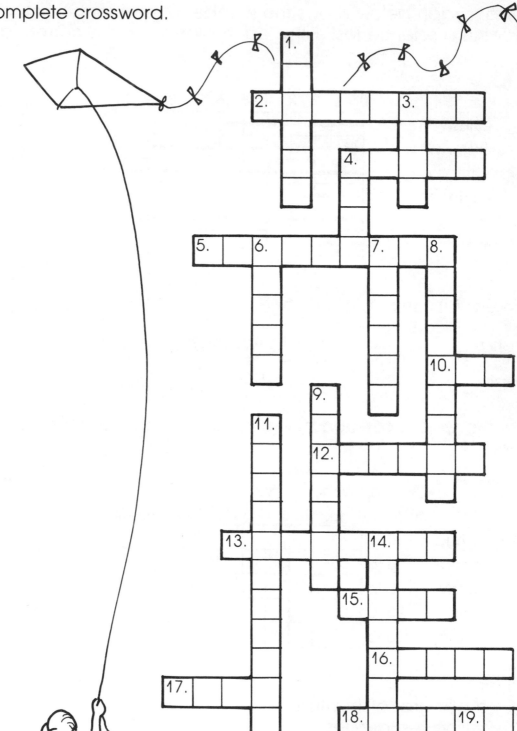
3. 3 ? 2 = 5
4. 2, 4, 6, 8
6. 3 ? 2 = 1
7. ÷
8. ▭
9. 1.5
11. –
14. >
19. ◓
20. 3, 5, 7, 9

Across

2. ×
4. =
5. 3)4 1 R1
10. +
12. ○
13. △
15. <
16. 3 ? 2 = 6
17. 5 – 5 = ?
18. ½

MULTIPLE CHOICE

Circle the correct answer.

	Example	a.	b.	c.	d.
1.	7481 − 3765	3,715	4,716	3,716	none of these
2.	86,107 − 59,476	26,631	27,631	27,632	none of these
3.	$\frac{3}{4} \times \frac{5}{7}$	$\frac{12}{26}$	$\frac{15}{28}$	$\frac{16}{29}$	none of these
4.	643 × 449	288,709	298,707	288,717	none of these
5.	$5\overline{)547}$	6 r-37	9 r-38	12	none of these
6.	$9 \times 7 \times 6 \times 4$	1412	1512	1612	none of these
7.	$1\frac{1}{2} \div 18$	$\frac{1}{12}$	$\frac{1}{18}$	$\frac{1}{2}$	none of these
8.	$31\overline{)9362}$	202	302	301	none of these
9.	$5\frac{3}{4}$ $+ 6\frac{1}{8}$	$10\frac{1}{2}$	$9\frac{7}{8}$	$8\frac{1}{8}$	none of these

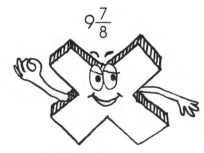
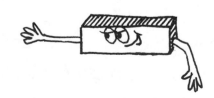

AVERAGING

Name_____

Find each class member's grade average. Also find the total class average.

	1	2	3	4	5	6	7	8	9	10	11	12	Avg.
Tanya	86	94	70	81	92	74	75	89	76	97	77	73	
Noel		76	90	79	80	73	76	96	88	100	88	78	
Greg	85		95	75	75	96		91	92			79	
Todd	71	87	90	91	89		75	95	97	87	84	80	
Brad		92		84	81		76	82		86	94		
Richard	85	92	96		71		85	94	89	78	74	86	
Parker	88	70	96	97		91	83		72	83	82	78	
Ragon	93		73		82		78	93	77			85	
Joey	90		98	78	81	94	74	73	98	79			
Chris	72	93	87		83	86		93		72	88	82	
Amber	100	90	98	77	90	70		95	91	82	87	88	
Donna	71	96				83		92	92		88	94	
Ed		89			95	100	72	75	92	81	79	82	
Cora	84	88		92	88	93	80	89	100		89	77	
Cheryl	74	79	86	98	84	78	100	80	85	81	81	94	
Carrie	74		99	96		99	100	94	70		82	87	
Ronnie	94	97	94	79		87		72	93	80	91	83	
Steve	75	87	98	77	86	99	84	94	97	79	80	100	
Fayne	76	86	100	73	87	94	81	90		87	91	81	
Vernon	70	86	72		88	93	71		71		99	79	
Sandra	77	88	98	88	79	96	82	89	78	100	92	89	
Lee	82		76	75	85		98	71		77	80	76	
Maureen	95		95	70		83	97	83	73	78	93	73	
Tom		42		51	63		100		31		75	51	
Ancil	97	77	70	81		92	83	88	74	90	80	70	
Sue	83	83	74	74	74	87	82	73	76	84	94	88	
Jackie	78		78		91	95					95	73	
Nancy	96	80		96	72	94	84	86	74	98	96	70	
Beth	79	71		82			78	85	76	77	99	100	
Jan	70		86	82	75	80		92	95	81	76	93	

Who has the highest average? _____

Who has the lowest average? _____

_____
class
average

AVERAGING

Name_____

Find the average score for each group of numbers. Put answers on line below each group.

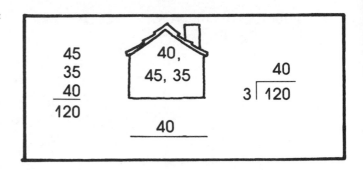

45
35
40
_____
120

40, 45, 35

$$\begin{array}{r} 40 \\ 3\overline{)120} \end{array}$$

40

202,85 172

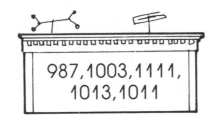

987,1003,1111, 1013,1011

_____

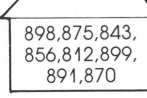

898,875,843, 856,812,899, 891,870

_____

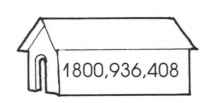

1800,936,408

_____

334,335, 439,449,629 231,222,189 169

_____

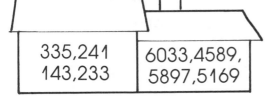

335,241 143,233

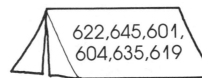

6033,4589, 5897,5169

_____

622,645,601, 604,635,619

_____

749,741,738, 799,710,799 721

_____

185,167,95 125,59,154,146

_____

536,584,555, 525,563,548, 585,464,

_____

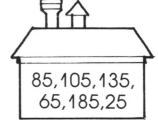

85,105,135, 65,185,25

_____

685,732, 497,841, 670

_____

445,863,112, 989,119,745 645,239,343

_____

1005,995, 1010,998, 992

_____

11,45,83,55, 69,74,3,12, 16,22

_____

799,739,941, 899,845,697, 1045,955

_____

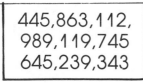

Math IF8744

95

ROUNDING

Name_____

Shade correctly rounded answers to find the
path to Skull Island.

9999 1000	7659 9000	6650 6000	239 300	9764 8000	4596 4000	9327 9000	3794 2000
3653 4000	5931 6000	5100 5000	4398 4000	8781 9000	59589 60000	3479 3000	6743 8000
7010 7000	3426 4000	7900 6000	4533 4000	9700 9000	1234 2000	6349 7000	4576 4000
2395 2000	1876 2000	6289 6000	2895 3000	16793 20000	1324 1000	55721 60000	87888 90000
9746 1000	3625 5000	3296 4000	5697 4000	7896 9000	4567 4000	8235 9000	27681 30000
92116 90000	7759 8000	66656 70000			2975 1000	76950 70000	751 800
63825 60000	237 300	5235 6000			2975 2000	1099 2000	8479 8000
31326 30000	1097 100	7659 7000	89657 80000	3974 3000	7695 9000	3265 2000	18618 20000
9191 9000	6253 7000	421 400	6667 7000	4989 5000	965 100	7543 7000	396 400
7861 8000	8235 9000	92381 90000	367 300	23515 20000	73921 70000	52352 50000	35479 40000
333 300	3457 4000	563 600	6295 7000	4325 5000	9234 10000	765 700	4326 5000
793 800	42431 40000	77216 80000	3279 4000	1099 2000	4976 4000	7695 7000	6959 6000

Math IF8744   96   © 1990 Instructional Fair, Inc.

GEOMETRY: AREA

Name_____

Find the area by counting square units.

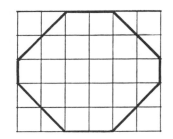

_____

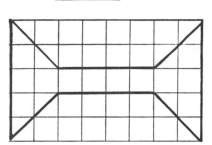

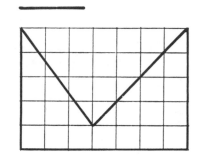

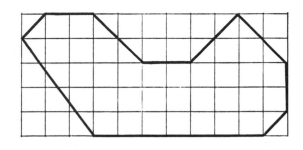

_____

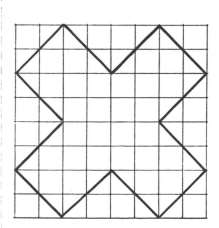

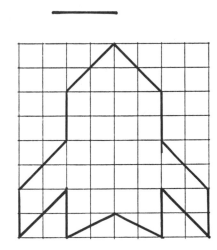

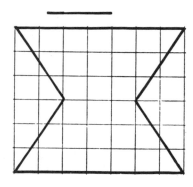

_____

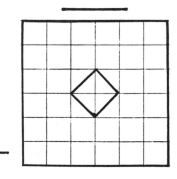

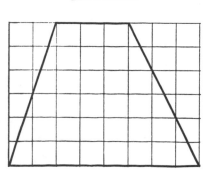

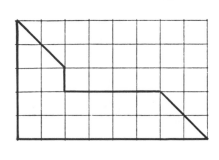

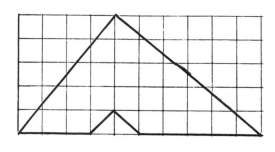

GEOMETRY: PERIMETER

Name_____

Find the perimeter of each figure.

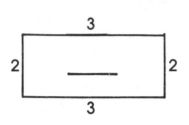

3
2   2
3

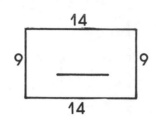

14
9   9
14

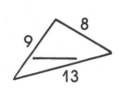

8
9
13

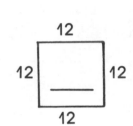

14
14   14
14

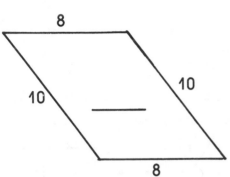

8
10   10
8

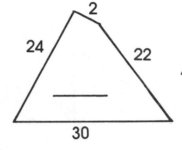

2
24   22
30

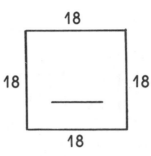

18
18   18
18

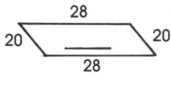

12
12   12
12

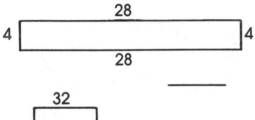

28
4   4
28

_____

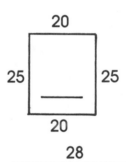

9
39   45

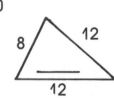

20
25   25
20

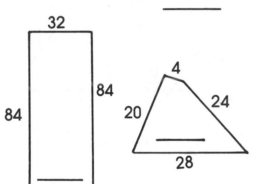

32
84   84
32

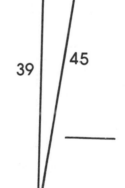

4
20   24
28

_____

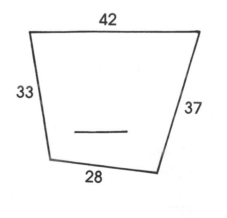

28
20   20
28

8   12
12

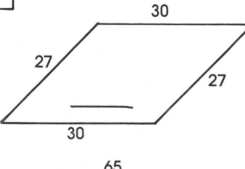

30
27   27
30

42
33   37
28

3
18   18
3

65
40   40
65

AREA AND PERIMETER

Name_____

Use drawings to answer puzzles.

Across

1.
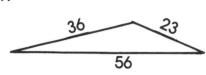

3.
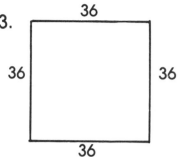

5.
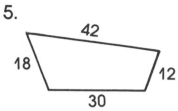

Down

1.
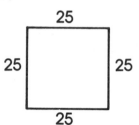

2.
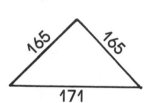

3.
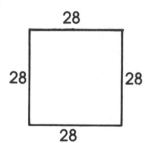

4.
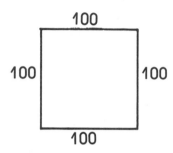

Perimeter

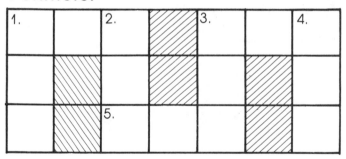

Across

1.

2.

3.
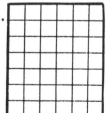

4.

5.
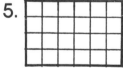

Down

1.
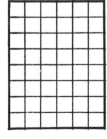

3.

2.

Area

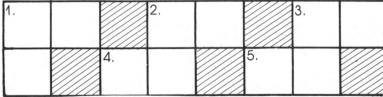

VOLUME

Volume is the measure of the inside of a space figure. Find the volume. Count the boxes.

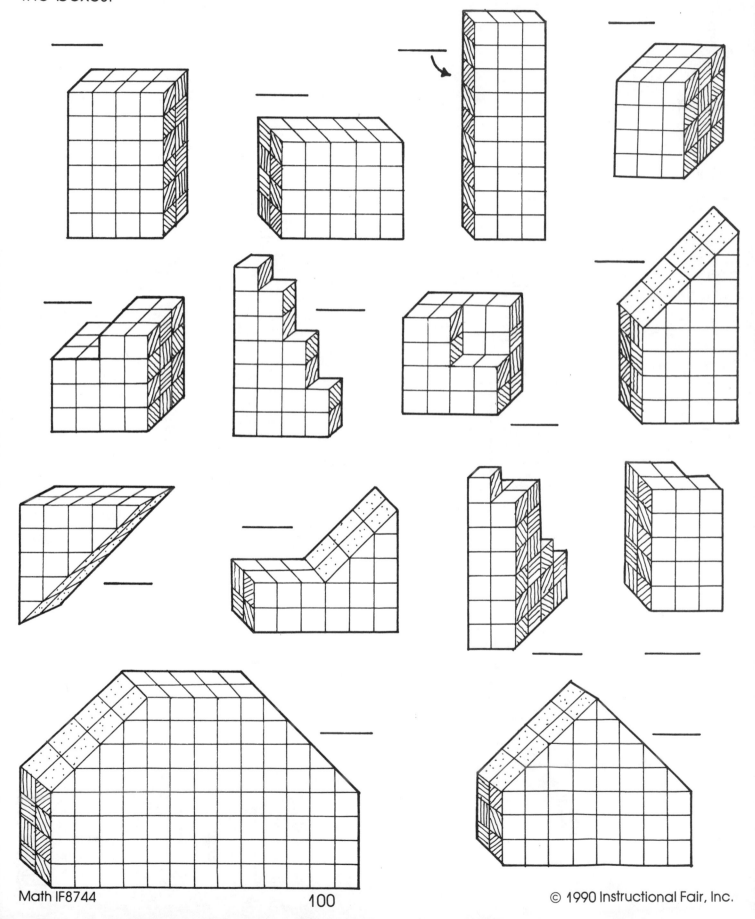

CROSS-NUMBER SUMMARY
(+ − × ÷)

Name_____

Work problems. Use answers to complete puzzles.

Across

1. 6175 ÷ 65
3. 770 ÷ 35
5. 21,590 ÷ 635
6. 8722 ÷ 89
7. 1848 ÷ 56
9. 5092 ÷ 67
11. 8100 ÷ 90
12. 1207 ÷ 71

Down

1. 9765 ÷ 105
2. 2916 ÷ 54
3. 2581 ÷ 89
4. 20,580 ÷ 735
7. 2964 ÷ 76
8. 1470 ÷ 49
9. 1207 ÷ 17
10. 5159 ÷ 77

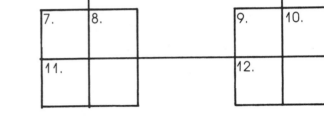

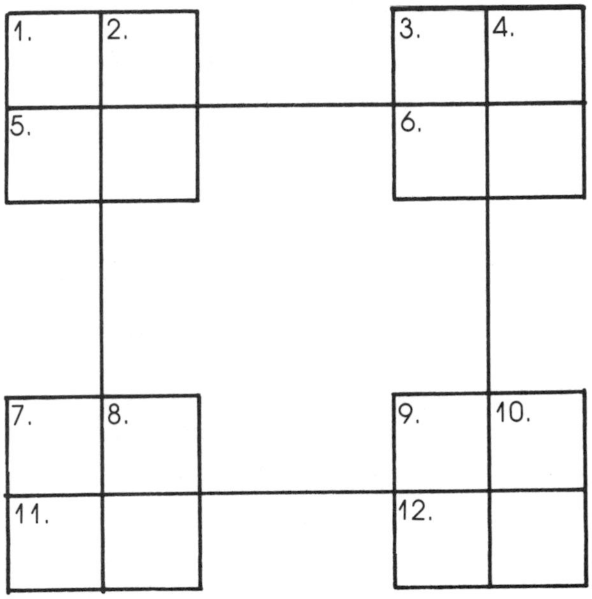

Down

1. 11 × 42
2. 22 − 14 + 16 − 9 + 33
3. 65 × 13
5. 38 × 23
6. 33 × 19
8. 186 + 157 + 199 + 153 + 189
9. 232 + 201 + 249 + 132
11. 1790 − 791
12. 336 + 301 + 323

Across

1. 32 × 14
4. 1290 − 606
5. 1721 − 859
7. 21 × 28
10. 89 + 67 + 58 + 61 + 43 + 70 + 91
12. 16 × 59
13. 26 × 36
14. 22 × 45

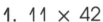

REVIEW: + − × ÷

Name_____

Use the shapes for clues to work problems.

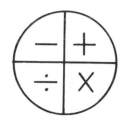

765	9	1288
96	65	15
12	8	56

Example

$\boxed{765}\ \div\ \boxed{9}\ =\ \_\_\_\_\_$ 　　　 $=\ \_\_\_\_\_$

$=\ \_\_\_\_\_$ 　　　 $=\ \_\_\_\_\_$

$=\ \_\_\_\_\_$ 　　　 $=\ \_\_\_\_\_$

$=\ \_\_\_\_\_$ 　　　 $=\ \_\_\_\_\_$

$=\ \_\_\_\_\_$ 　　　 $=\ \_\_\_\_\_$

$=\ \_\_\_\_\_$ 　　　 $=\ \_\_\_\_\_$

$=\ \_\_\_\_\_$ 　　　 $=\ \_\_\_\_\_$

$=\ \_\_\_\_\_$ 　　　 $=\ \_\_\_\_\_$

$=\ \_\_\_\_\_$ 　　　 $=\ \_\_\_\_\_$

$=\ \_\_\_\_\_$ 　　　 $=\ \_\_\_\_\_$

Math IF8744　　　102　　　© 1990 Instructional Fair, Inc.

Answer Key

Page 1

READING and WRITING NUMBERS

Name_____

35,634	Thirty-five thousand, six hundred thirty-four
6,000,900	Six million, nine hundred
200,000,004	Two hundred million, four

Read the following numbers.

1. 900,702   3,004,081   9,421,620
2. 7,490,378   89,500,100   206,220,800
3. 8,004,500   69,521,001   260,090,210

Write the correct numeral for each number.

1. Five hundred sixty-two thousand, one hundred seventy-four **562,174**

2. Two hundred million, five hundred eighteen thousand, seven hundred thirty-six **200,518,736**

3. Sixty-five billion, two hundred seventy million, nine hundred forty-eight thousand, three hundred one **65,270,948,301**

4. Nine trillion, four hundred sixty billion, seven hundred twelve million, nineteen thousand, five hundred three **9,460,712,019,503**

Challenge
Rearrange each group of numbers from smallest to largest.

37,049,757	36,049,957	34,049,858
34,049,858	**36,049,957**	**37,049,757**
36,491,956	36,126,851	36,490,856
36,126,851	**36,490,856**	**36,491,956**

Page 1

Page 2

PLACE VALUE

Name_____

Ten-Thousands	Thousands	Hundreds	Tens	Ones
8	8	8	8	8

Look carefully at the number above, note that 8 has a different value, and that this value depends upon the place the figure holds in a number. Each 8 is 10 times the value of the 8 to the right of it.

The value of a figure depends upon the place it holds in a number.

1. In the number 5,356,919, what is the value of each number?

5 means _____5,000,000_____
3 means _____300,000_____
5 means _____50,000_____
6 means _____6,000_____
9 means _____900_____
1 means _____10_____
9 means _____9_____

2. In each set, draw a circle around the largest number. Underline the smallest number.

8,651,233	1,863,741,908	(5,423,416,814)
(8,653,234)	1,853,743,907	5,423,416,014
8,555,229	(1,863,745,906)	5,423,416,804

6,439,016,213	(105,023,010,001)	(2,416,029,786)
(7,230,104,203)	105,003,010,001	2,406,029,786
6,439,015,213	105,023,000,001	2,410,009,786

Page 2

Page 3

CHECKING ADDITION and SUBTRACTION

Name_____

Example	Check	
584 + 297 881	297 + 584 881	Check addition by adding in reverse.
701 − 466 235	235 + 466 701	Check subtraction with addition.

Check each problem for accuracy. Write T for true and F for false.

1. 28,153
− 17,745
10,408   **T**

2. 49,853
+ 83,289
132,132   **F**

3. 8,466
+ 7,907
16,373   **T**

4. 84,542
− 9,368
75,174   **T**

5. 642,017
− 568,726
73,291   **T**

6. 7,431
+ 6,214
14,745   **F**

7. 52,814
+ 7,623
60,437   **T**

8. 74,222
+ 6,787
80,419   **F**

9. 872
− 593
379   **F**

10. 8,466
+ 7,907
16,373   **T**

11. 3,001
− 597
2,403   **F**

12. 7,210
+ 6,143
13,353   **T**

Page 3

Page 4

ADDITION

Name_____

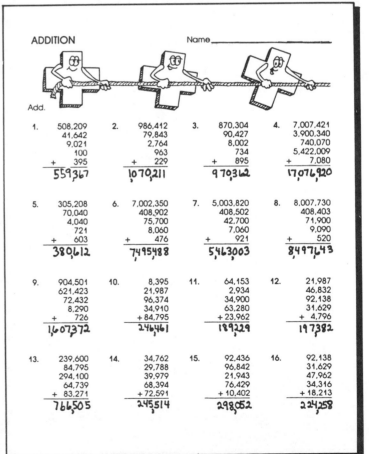

Add.

1. 508,209
41,642
9,021
100
+ 395
559,367

2. 986,412
79,843
2,764
963
+ 229
1,070,211

3. 870,304
90,427
8,002
734
+ 895
970,362

4. 7,007,421
3,900,340
740,070
5,422,009
+ 7,080
17,076,920

5. 305,208
70,040
4,040
721
+ 603
380,612

6. 7,002,350
408,902
75,700
8,060
+ 476
7,495,488

7. 5,003,820
408,502
42,700
7,060
+ 921
5,463,003

8. 8,007,730
408,403
71,900
9,090
+ 520
8,497,643

9. 904,501
621,423
72,432
8,290
+ 726
1,607,372

10. 8,395
21,987
96,374
34,910
+ 84,795
246,461

11. 64,153
2,934
34,900
63,280
+ 23,962
189,229

12. 21,987
46,832
92,138
31,629
+ 4,796
197,382

13. 239,600
84,795
294,100
64,739
+ 83,271
766,505

14. 34,762
29,788
39,979
68,394
+ 72,591
245,514

15. 92,436
96,842
21,943
76,429
+ 10,402
298,052

16. 92,138
31,629
47,962
34,316
+ 18,213
224,258

Page 4

Math IF8744   103   © 1990 Instructional Fair, Inc.

Answer Key

Page 5

ADDITION   Name_____

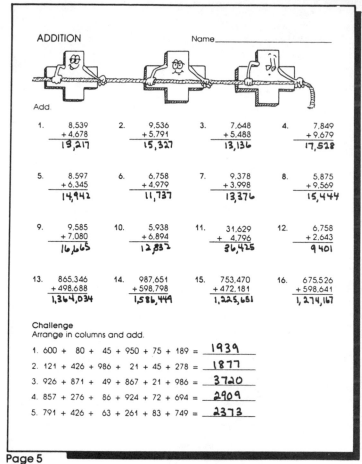

Add.

1. 8,539 + 4,678 = **13,217**	2. 9,536 + 5,791 = **15,327**	3. 7,648 + 5,488 = **13,136**	4. 7,849 + 9,679 = **17,528**
5. 8,597 + 6,345 = **14,942**	6. 6,758 + 4,979 = **11,737**	7. 9,378 + 3,998 = **13,376**	8. 5,875 + 9,569 = **15,444**
9. 9,585 + 7,080 = **16,665**	10. 5,938 + 6,894 = **12,832**	11. 31,629 + 4,796 = **36,425**	12. 6,758 + 2,643 = **9,401**
13. 865,346 + 498,688 = **1,364,034**	14. 987,651 + 598,798 = **1,586,449**	15. 753,470 + 472,181 = **1,225,651**	16. 675,526 + 598,641 = **1,274,167**

Challenge
Arrange in columns and add.

1. 600 + 80 + 45 + 950 + 75 + 189 = **1939**
2. 121 + 426 + 986 + 21 + 45 + 278 = **1877**
3. 926 + 871 + 49 + 867 + 21 + 986 = **3720**
4. 857 + 276 + 86 + 924 + 72 + 694 = **2909**
5. 791 + 426 + 63 + 261 + 83 + 749 = **2373**

Page 5

Page 6

ADDITION   Name_____

1. 921,206 + 92,126 + 4,201 + 960 + 420 = **1,018,913**
2. 629,437 + 76,829 + 9,100 + 265 + 786 = **716,417**
3. 776,824 + 81,429 + 9,600 + 422 + 861 = **869,136**
4. 878,204 + 26,749 + 1,322 + 687 + 682 = **907,644**
5. 286,400 + 63,721 + 7,834 + 821 + 20 = **358,796**
6. 999,999 + 88,888 + 7,777 + 666 + 555 = **1,097,885**
7. 426,699 + 72,432 + 6,210 + 427 + 563 = **506,331**
8. 291,426 + 63,487 + 7,648 + 876 + 635 = **364,072**
9. 4,002,330 + 704,906 + 72,700 + 9,160 + 580 = **4,789,676**
10. 1,008,400 + 4,900,640 + 740,160 + 8,440,003 + 8,102 = **15,097,305**
11. 6,005,600 + 7,009,420 + 560,051 + 4,328,008 + 6,321 = **17,909,400**
12. 3,005,600 + 205,320 + 71,426 + 2,600 + 126 = **3,285,072**
13. 9,005,720 + 280,302 + 63,500 + 8,429 + 624 = **9,558,575**
14. 12,000 + 250 + 4,603 + 186 + 404 = **17,443**
15. 5,001 + 105 + 20,405 + 4,631 + 221 = **30,363**
16. 7,864,200 + 695,154 + 86,423 + 1,500 + 786 = **8,648,063**
17. 94,983 + 69,787 + 74,978 + 68,666 + 39,789 + 87,878 = **436,081**
18. 79,935 + 86,940 + 30,979 + 85,398 + 74,297 + 68,849 = **426,398**

Page 6

Page 7

ADDITION   Name_____

Work problems. Shade in answers on motorcycle hill to climb path. A blank represents a fall.

763,821 + 937,265 = **1,701,086**	871,135 + 680,012 = **1,551,147**	843,753 + 629,441 = **1,473,194**	4,922 + 1,487 = **6,409**	7,270 + 1,985 = **9,255**	1,905 + 2,184 = **4,089**
9,648 + 44 + 738 = **10,430**	437 + 12 + 9,256 = **9,705**	7,005 + 428 + 5,675 = **13,108**	8,462 + 729 + 41 = **9,232**	438 + 9,511 + 473 = **10,422**	9,613 + 382 + 1,834 = **11,829**

8405 + 236 + 4027 = **12,668**	7248 + 651 + 4003 = **11,902**	3421 + 9806 + 3349 = **16,576**	529 + 4604 + 4060 = **9193**	8623 + 9585 + 2434 = **20,642**
3928 + 8296 + 9386 + 4625 + 1821 = **28,056**	8123 + 4758 + 4385 + 5372 + 8272 = **30,910**	3408 + 1385 + 5723 + 3954 + 3976 = **18,446**	8753 + 3964 + 8342 + 3632 + 4632 = **29,323**	9305 + 3057 + 3268 + 2385 + 3705 = **21,720**
2176 + 4382 + 7143 = **13,701**	5841 + 8305 + 2318 = **16,464**	4060 + 3114 + 2379 = **9553**	3495 + 7354 + 6372 = **17,221**	7923 + 2548 + 7836 = **18,307**

Motorcycle hill (path numbers):
Left: 9,193 / 18,576 / 1,701,086 / 10,902 / 10,430 / 17,221 / 12,902 / 9,553 / 11,829 / 9,089 / 30,910 / 1,473,194 / 5,702 / 1,473,194 / 18,751

Right: 10,422 / 12,668 / 1,499 / 14,992 / 29,323 / 9,293 / 9,285 / 8,193 / 28,056 / 21,710 / 20,642 / 1,551,147 / 15,207 / 9,232 / 28,056 / 16,464

Which rider made it to the top with the least falls? **1**

Page 7

Page 8

BASIC REVIEW: + −   Name_____

Complete the number sentences.

892	−	547	+	234	=	**579**
−		−		−		−
392	−	166	+	207	=	**433**
+		+		+		+
198	−	74	+	59	=	**183**
=		=		=		=
698	−	**455**	+	**86**	=	**329**

415	+	362	−	194	=	**583**
+		+		+		+
277	+	409	−	384	=	**302**
−		−		−		−
306	+	211	−	186	=	**331**
=		=		=		=
386	+	**560**	−	**392**	=	**554**

321	+	156	+	284	=	**761**
−		−		−		−
58	+	39	+	73	=	**170**
−		−		−		−
14	+	85	+	102	=	**201**
=		=		=		=
249	+	**32**	+	**109**	=	**390**

625	+	107	+	211	=	**943**
−		−		−		−
436	+	28	+	65	=	**529**
−		−		−		−
109	+	17	+	83	=	**209**
=		=		=		=
80	+	**62**	+	**63**	=	**205**

Page 8

Answer Key

Page 9

REVIEW — Name_____

Follow the directions to find the hidden treasure at the bottom of the Indian Ocean. If you make no errors, the final answer will be 0.

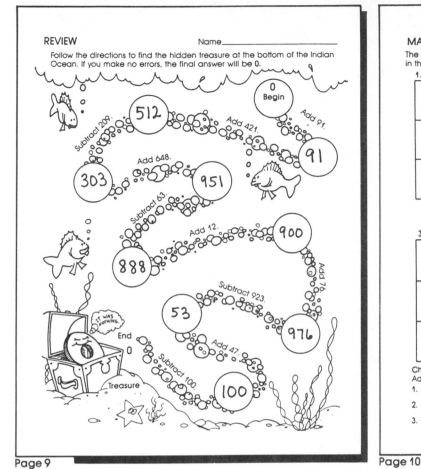

0 Begin
Add 91. → 91
Add 421. 512
Subtract 209. 303
Add 648. 951
Add 76 → 900
Subtract 63. 888
Add 12.
Subtract 923. 53
976
Subtract 100. 100
Add 47.
End 0
Treasure

Page 9

Page 10

MAGIC SQUARES — Name_____

The sum of each row, column and diagonal is the same in a magic square. Fill in the blanks.

1.
7	14	15
20	12	4
9	10	17

2.
2	7	6
9	5	1
4	3	8

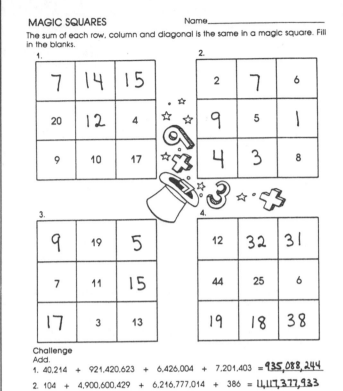

3.
9	19	5
7	11	15
17	3	13

4.
12	32	31
44	25	6
19	18	38

Challenge
Add.

1. 40,214 + 921,420,623 + 6,426,004 + 7,201,403 = **935,088,244**

2. 104 + 4,900,600,429 + 6,216,777,014 + 386 = **11,117,377,933**

3. 9,004,276 + 621,924,104 + 666 + 7,871 = **630,936,917**

Page 10

Page 11

ESTIMATING SUMS — Name_____

Rounding is an easy way to find out how many in all.

	Nearest Ten.		Nearest Hundred		Nearest Thousand
39	40	421	400	989	1,000
+48	+50	+499	+500	+1,421	+1,000
	90		900		2,000

1. 86 / +43 → 90 +40 **130**
2. 21 / +89 → 20 +90 **110**
3. 98 / +32 → 100 +30 **130**
4. 836 / +295 → 800 +300 **1100**
5. 821 / +69 → 800 +70 **870**
6. 271 / +126 → 300 +100 **400**
7. 1,423 / +989 → 1000 +1000 **2000**
8. 8,321 / +7,894 → 8000 +8000 **16000**
9. 6,431 / +2,986 → 6000 +3000 **9000**
10. 793 / +16 → 800 +20 **820**
11. 2,426 / +149 → 2000 +100 **2100**
12. 621 / +599 → 600 +600 **1200**
13. 1,639 / +403 → 2000 +400 **2400**
14. 8,798 / +8,640 → 9000 +9000 **18000**
15. 9,198 / +8,102 → 9000 +8000 **17000**

Challenge
Michael went to the Sports Center. He bought a helmet for $29.99, a sweat shirt for $9.49 and a pair of running shoes for $52.99. Estimate what Michael spent.
$92

Page 11

Page 12

SUBTRACTION — Name_____

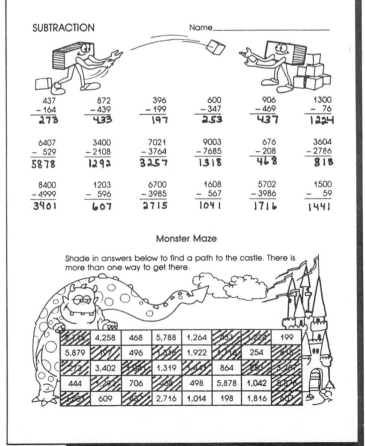

437 −164 = **273**	872 −439 = **433**	396 −199 = **197**	600 −347 = **253**	906 −469 = **437**	1300 −76 = **1224**
6407 −529 = **5878**	3400 −2108 = **1292**	7021 −3764 = **3257**	9003 −7685 = **1318**	676 −208 = **468**	3604 −2786 = **818**
8400 −4999 = **3401**	1203 −596 = **607**	6700 −3985 = **2715**	1608 −567 = **1041**	5702 −3986 = **1716**	1500 −59 = **1441**

Monster Maze

Shade in answers below to find a path to the castle. There is more than one way to get there.

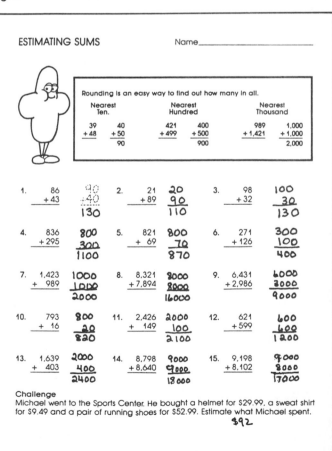

	4,258	468	5,788	1,264			199
5,879		496		1,922		254	
	3,402		1,319		864		
444		706		498	5,878	1,042	
	609		2,716	1,014	198	1,816	

Page 12

Math IF8744   105   © 1990 Instructional Fair, Inc.

Answer Key

Page 13

SUBTRACTION
Name_____

Work problems. Use answers to name the puppies. Match names with answers.
One is left for you to name.

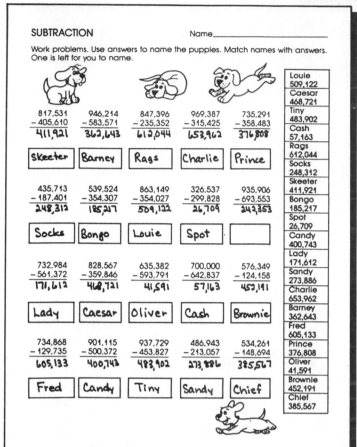

817,531 − 405,610 **411,921**	946,214 − 583,571 **362,643**	847,396 − 235,352 **612,044**	969,387 − 315,425 **653,962**	735,291 − 358,483 **376,808**
Skeeter	Barney	Rags	Charlie	Prince

435,713 − 187,401 **248,312**	539,524 − 354,307 **185,217**	863,149 − 354,027 **509,122**	326,537 − 299,828 **26,709**	935,906 − 693,553 **242,353**
Socks	Bongo	Louie	Spot	

732,984 − 561,372 **171,612**	828,567 − 359,846 **468,721**	635,382 − 593,791 **41,591**	700,000 − 642,837 **57,163**	576,349 − 124,158 **452,191**
Lady	Caesar	Oliver	Cash	Brownie

734,868 − 129,735 **605,133**	901,115 − 500,372 **400,743**	937,729 − 453,827 **483,902**	486,943 − 213,057 **273,886**	534,261 − 148,694 **385,567**
Fred	Candy	Tiny	Sandy	Chief

Louie 509,122
Caesar 468,721
Tiny 483,902
Cash 57,163
Rags 612,044
Socks 248,312
Skeeter 411,921
Bongo 185,217
Spot 26,709
Candy 400,743
Lady 171,612
Sandy 273,886
Charlie 653,962
Barney 362,643
Fred 605,133
Prince 376,808
Oliver 41,591
Brownie 452,191
Chief 385,567

Page 13

Page 14

SUBTRACTION: Larger Numbers
Name_____

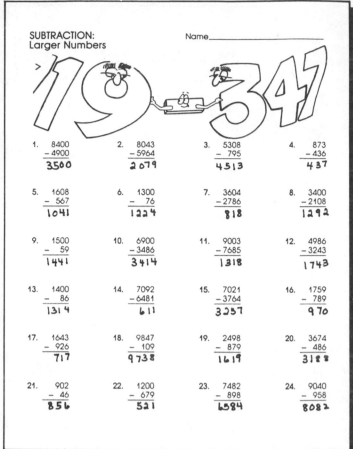

1. 8400 − 4900 **3500**	2. 8043 − 5964 **2079**	3. 5308 − 795 **4513**	4. 873 − 436 **437**
5. 1608 − 567 **1041**	6. 1300 − 76 **1224**	7. 3604 − 2786 **818**	8. 3400 − 2108 **1292**
9. 1500 − 59 **1441**	10. 6900 − 3486 **3414**	11. 9003 − 7685 **1318**	12. 4986 − 3243 **1743**
13. 1400 − 86 **1314**	14. 7092 − 6481 **611**	15. 7021 − 3764 **3257**	16. 1759 − 789 **970**
17. 1643 − 926 **717**	18. 9847 − 109 **9738**	19. 2498 − 879 **1619**	20. 3674 − 486 **3188**
21. 902 − 46 **856**	22. 1200 − 679 **521**	23. 7482 − 898 **6584**	24. 9040 − 958 **8082**

Page 14

Page 15

SUBTRACTION
Name_____

Work the baseball problems. Each answer found on the bat represents a
homerun. How many homeruns were hit? **8**

62111   1184   37785   3091   37786   6135   322   2118   5631   2371   5256   5646   2615   4431   7287

3118 − 1207 **1911**	9893 − 7521 **2372**	9217 − 375 **8842**	7354 − 4739 **2615**	5806 − 560 **5246**
5008 − 4201 **807**	3468 − 2384 **1084**	7975 − 805 **7170**	7672 − 4291 **3381**	6760 − 2125 **4635**
90,006 − 52,221 **37,785**	4382 − 761 **3621**	8779 − 5137 **3642**	1725 − 1413 **312**	9372 − 3741 **5631**
4537 − 2519 **2018**	1,834,216 − 1,772,105 **62,111**	3448 − 2374 **1074**	7352 − 65 **7287**	5738 − 92 **5646**
43,026 − 219 **42,807**	9987 − 3852 **6135**	6172 − 3081 **3091**	4357 − 26 **4331**	8710 − 14 **8696**

Page 15

Page 16

ZEROS in SUBTRACTION
Name_____

6,040 − 406 5,634	6,000 − 407 5,593	6,000 − 400 5,600	6,004 − 407 5,597

Subtract and check.

1. 402.01 − 20.40 **381.61**	2. 606.09 − 40.80 **565.29**	3. 800.05 − 50.09 **749.96**	4. 605.90 − 50.70 **555.20**
5. 8.050 − 508 **7542**	6. 8,000 − 406 **7594**	7. 40.30 − 1.06 **39.24**	8. 7,060 − 708 **6352**
9. 90,000 − 4,638 **85,362**	10. 70,000 − 2,975 **67,025**	11. 60,004 − 5,007 **54,997**	12. 80,406 − 7,012 **73,394**
13. 80,002 − 3,008 **76,994**	14. 40,006 − 3,216 **36,790**	15. 3,000 − 107 **2893**	16. 70,081 − 4,200 **65,881**
17. 60,027 − 55,575 **4452**	18. 68,370 − 6,400 **61,970**	19. 64,900 − 63,289 **1611**	20. 9,489 − 6,766 **2723**
21. 46,000 − 9,826 **36,174**	22. 60,000 − 54,789 **5211**	23. 98,900 − 83,721 **15,179**	24. 46,920 − 8,649 **38,271**

Page 16

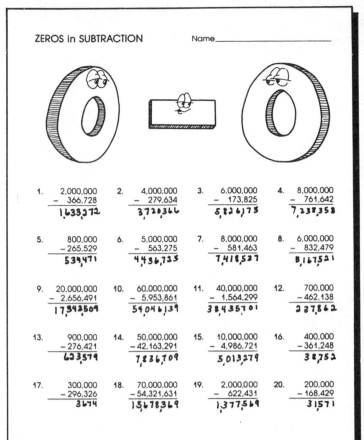

ZEROS in SUBTRACTION — Name_____

1. 2,000,000 − 366,728 = 1,633,272
2. 4,000,000 − 279,634 = 3,720,366
3. 6,000,000 − 173,825 = 5,826,175
4. 8,000,000 − 761,642 = 7,238,358
5. 800,000 − 265,529 = 534,471
6. 5,000,000 − 563,275 = 4,436,725
7. 8,000,000 − 581,463 = 7,418,537
8. 6,000,000 − 832,479 = 5,167,521
9. 20,000,000 − 2,656,491 = 17,343,509
10. 60,000,000 − 5,953,861 = 54,046,139
11. 40,000,000 − 1,564,299 = 38,435,701
12. 700,000 − 462,138 = 237,862
13. 900,000 − 276,421 = 623,579
14. 50,000,000 − 42,163,291 = 7,836,709
15. 10,000,000 − 4,986,721 = 5,013,279
16. 400,000 − 361,248 = 38,752
17. 300,000 − 296,326 = 3,674
18. 70,000,000 − 54,321,631 = 15,678,369
19. 2,000,000 − 622,431 = 1,377,569
20. 200,000 − 168,429 = 31,571

Page 17

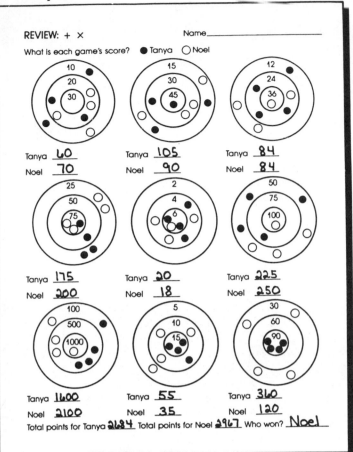

REVIEW: + × — Name_____

What is each game's score? ● Tanya ○ Noel

Tanya 60 / Noel 70
Tanya 105 / Noel 90
Tanya 84 / Noel 84
Tanya 175 / Noel 200
Tanya 20 / Noel 18
Tanya 225 / Noel 250
Tanya 1600 / Noel 2100
Tanya 55 / Noel 35
Tanya 360 / Noel 120

Total points for Tanya 2684   Total points for Noel 2967   Who won? Noel

Page 18

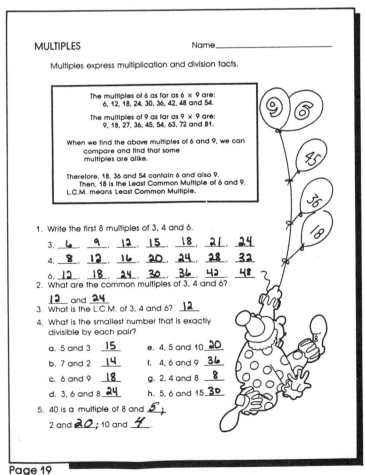

MULTIPLES — Name_____

Multiples express multiplication and division facts.

> The multiples of 6 as far as 6 × 9 are:
> 6, 12, 18, 24, 30, 36, 42, 48 and 54.
>
> The multiples of 9 as far as 9 × 9 are:
> 9, 18, 27, 36, 45, 54, 63, 72 and 81.
>
> When we find the above multiples of 6 and 9, we can compare and find that some multiples are alike.
>
> Therefore, 18, 36 and 54 contain 6 and also 9.
> Then, 18 is the Least Common Multiple of 6 and 9.
> L.C.M. means Least Common Multiple.

1. Write the first 8 multiples of 3, 4 and 6.
   3. 6, 9, 12, 15, 18, 21, 24
   4. 8, 12, 16, 20, 24, 28, 32
   6. 12, 18, 24, 30, 36, 42, 48
2. What are the common multiples of 3, 4 and 6? 12 and 24
3. What is the L.C.M. of 3, 4 and 6? 12
4. What is the smallest number that is exactly divisible by each pair?
   a. 5 and 3 — 15
   b. 7 and 2 — 14
   c. 6 and 9 — 18
   d. 3, 6 and 8 — 24
   e. 4, 5 and 10 — 20
   f. 4, 6 and 9 — 36
   g. 2, 4 and 8 — 8
   h. 5, 6 and 15 — 30
5. 40 is a multiple of 8 and 5; 2 and 20; 10 and 4.

Page 19

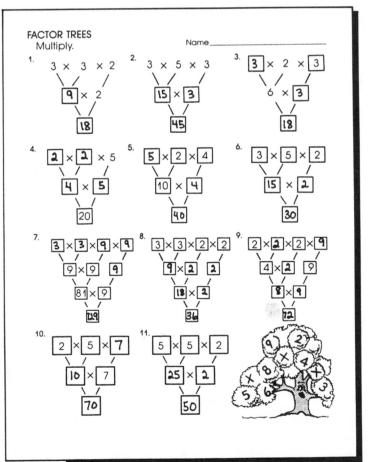

FACTOR TREES — Multiply. — Name_____

1. 3 × 3 × 2 → 9 × 2 → 18
2. 3 × 5 × 3 → 15 × 3 → 45
3. 3 × 2 × 3 → 6 × 3 → 18
4. 2 × 2 × 5 → 4 × 5 → 20
5. 5 × 2 × 4 → 10 × 4 → 40
6. 3 × 5 × 2 → 15 × 2 → 30
7. 3 × 3 × 9 × 9 → 9 × 9 × 9 → 81 × 9 → 729
8. 3 × 3 × 2 × 2 → 9 × 2 × 2 → 18 × 2 → 36
9. 2 × 2 × 2 × 9 → 4 × 2 × 9 → 8 × 9 → 72
10. 2 × 5 × 7 → 10 × 7 → 70
11. 5 × 5 × 2 → 25 × 2 → 50

Page 20

Answer Key

Page 21

MULTIPLICATION   Name_____

The pioneers have just had their first major set-back. All four wheels fell off their covered wagon going through the dangerous Rocky Mountains. You can help them put the wheels back on by multiplying each complete wheel.

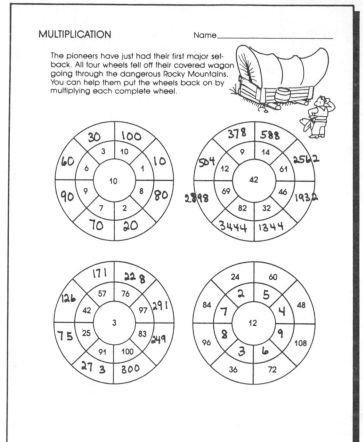

Page 22

MULTIPLICATION FACTS   Name_____

Multiplication facts 2 through 9
×	8
6	48
2	16
1	8

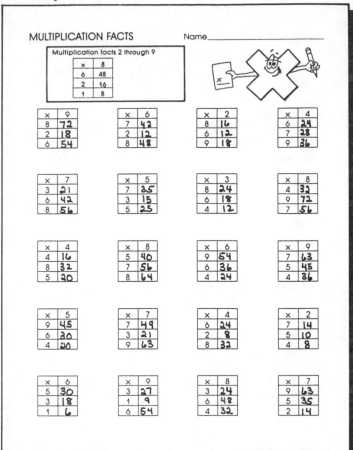

×	9		×	6		×	2		×	4
8	72		7	42		8	16		6	24
2	18		2	12		6	12		7	28
6	54		8	48		9	18		9	36

×	7		×	5		×	3		×	8
3	21		7	35		8	24		4	32
6	42		3	15		6	18		9	72
8	56		5	25		4	12		7	56

×	4		×	8		×	6		×	9
4	16		5	40		9	54		7	63
8	32		7	56		6	36		5	45
5	20		8	64		4	24		4	36

×	5		×	7		×	4		×	2
9	45		7	49		6	24		7	14
6	30		3	21		2	8		5	10
4	20		9	63		8	32		4	8

×	6		×	9		×	8		×	7
5	30		3	27		3	24		9	63
3	18		1	9		6	48		5	35
1	6		6	54		4	32		2	14

Page 23

MULTIPLICATION   Name_____

The arrows show which two numbers to multiply and where to write the answer.

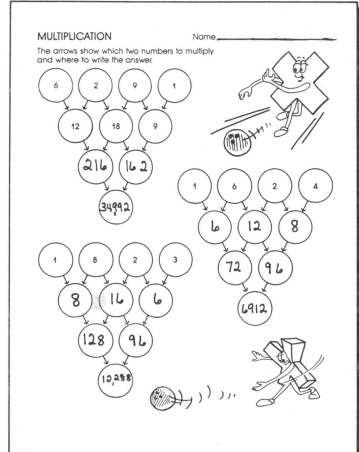

Page 24

MULTIPLICATION   Name_____

Remember: Any number times zero equals zero.

1.	905 × 7 = **6335**	2.	800 × 9 = **7200**	3.	804 × 6 = **4824**	4.	470 × 8 = **3760**
5.	709 × 6 = **4254**	6.	500 × 6 = **3000**	7.	900 × 8 = **7200**	8.	608 × 6 = **3648**
9.	428 × 6 = **2568**	10.	890 × 5 = **4450**	11.	720 × 4 = **2880**	12.	420 × 5 = **2100**
13.	576 × 2 = **1152**	14.	530 × 7 = **3710**	15.	970 × 3 = **2910**	16.	700 × 9 = **6300**
17.	638 × 6 = **3828**	18.	497 × 8 = **3976**	19.	982 × 7 = **6874**	20.	631 × 7 = **4417**
21.	707 × 6 = **4242**	22.	940 × 8 = **7520**	23.	290 × 6 = **1740**	24.	874 × 0 = **0**
25.	9204 × 7 = **64,428**	26.	8649 × 8 = **69,192**	27.	4309 × 7 = **30,163**	28.	6402 × 5 = **32,010**

Answer Key

Page 25

THREE-PLACE MULTIPLIER   Name_____

I.		II.	III.
468 Multiplicand		987	850
×375 Multiplier		×645	×470
2340 1st Partial Product		4935	000
3276 2nd Partial Product		3948	5150
1404 3rd Partial Product		5922	3400
175500 Product		636615	391500

1. 804 ×408 = 6432, 32160, **328,032**
2. 700 ×840 = 28000, 5600, **588,000**
3. 500 ×902 = 1000, 45000, **451,000**
4. 608 ×240 = 24320, 1216, **145,920**

5. 678 ×386 = 4068, 5424, 2034, **261,708**
6. 762 ×691 = 762, 6858, 4572, **526,542**
7. 398 ×421 = 398, 796, 1592, **167,558**
8. 709 ×284 = 2836, 5672, 1418, **201,356**

9. 703 ×307 = 4921, 21090, **215,821**
10. 843 ×658 = 6744, 4215, 5058, **554,694**
11. 504 ×405 = 2520, 20160, **204,120**
12. 200 ×607 = 1400, 12000, **121,400**

13. 874 ×981 = 874, 6992, 7866, **857,394**
14. 426 ×721 = 426, 852, 2982, **307,146**
15. 638 ×247 = 4466, 2552, 1276, **157,586**
16. 150 ×342 = 300, 600, 450, **51,300**

Page 26

MULTIPLICATION   Name_____

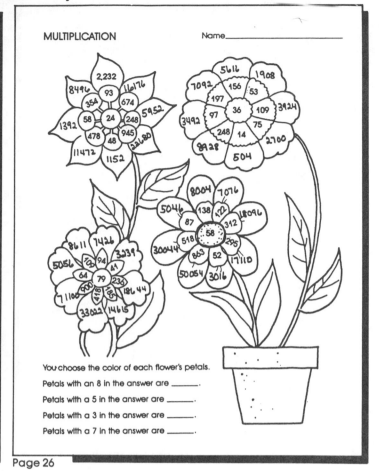

You choose the color of each flower's petals.

Petals with an 8 in the answer are _____.

Petals with a 5 in the answer are _____.

Petals with a 3 in the answer are _____.

Petals with a 7 in the answer are _____.

Page 26

Page 27

Name_____

Can you help me complete the web? To fill in the last ring, multiply the number in the center and keep multiplying in a straight line from the center. Remember, a spider's lifetime is short, so don't waste any time.

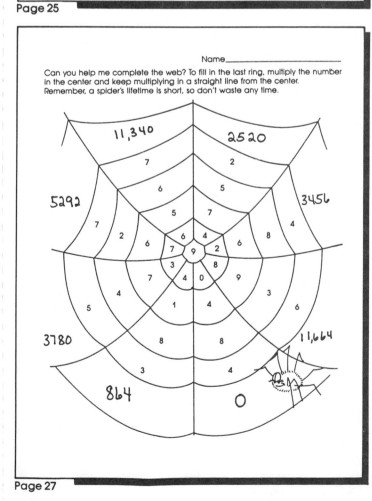

11,340   2520   5292   3456   3780   11,664   864   0

Page 27

Page 28

DIVISION: 1-Digit Divisor   Name_____

Work problems. Give the clowns with remainders a happy face ☺. Give the clowns without remainders a sad face ☹.

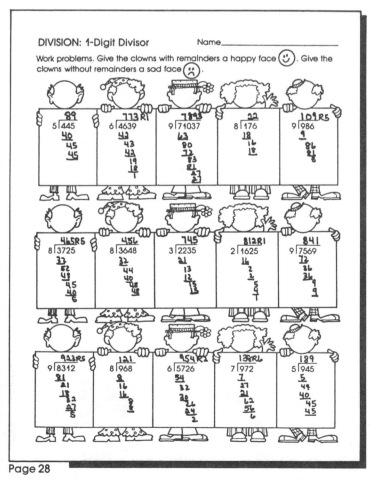

Answer Key

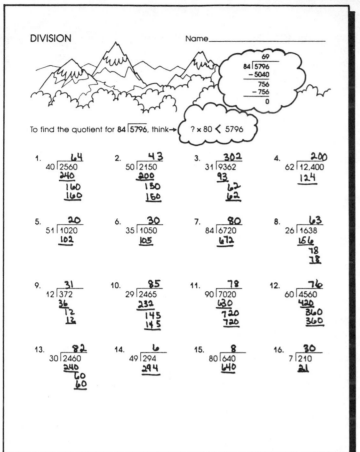

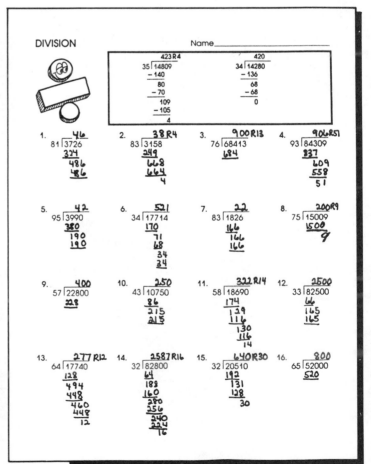

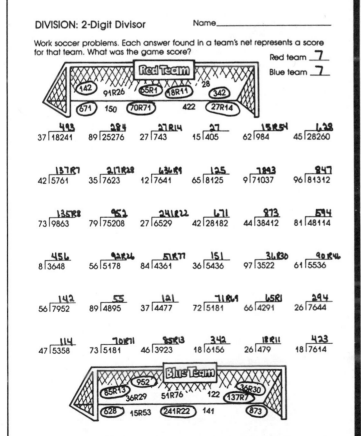

DIVISION

110

Answer Key

Page 33

DIVISION: 2-Digit Divisor Name_____

Work problems. Shade in the letters of those problems that have remainders to reveal the "ancient one"

A. 42)8799 = 209R21 B. 33)9278 = 281R5 C. 72)38952 = 541 D. 43)28939 = 673 E. 52)336 = 6R24

F. 26)16822 = 647 G. 58)22388 = 386 H. 27)743 = 27R14 I. 57)20406 = 358 J. 35)296 = 8R16

K. 62)984 = 15R54 L. 42)5761 = 137R7 M. 38)8056 = 212 N. 36)28404 = 789 O. 35)7623 = 217R28

P. 62)6735 = 108R39 Q. 26)1664 = 64 R. 46)419 = 9R5 S. 84)6552 = 78 T. 17)9741 = 573

U. 52)4628 = 89 V. 17)6145 = 361R8 W. 41)8173 = 199R14 X. 39)5304 = 136 Y. 66)6930 = 105

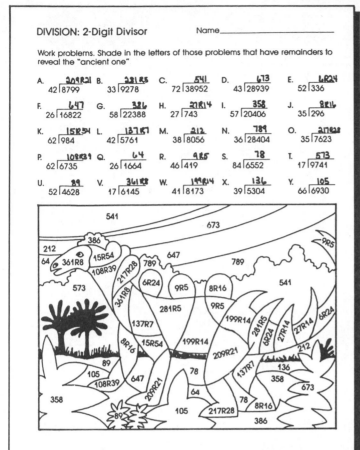

Page 34

DIVISION Name_____

Divide each problem. Draw a line connecting each problem to its answer.

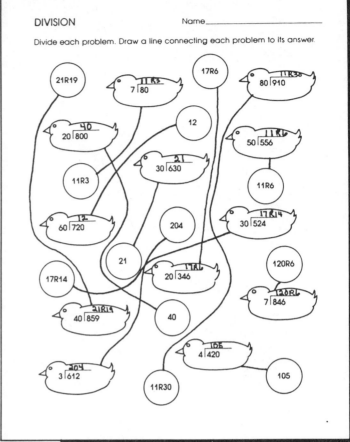

21R19 · 7)80 = 11R3 · 17R6 · 80)910 = 11R30 · 12 · 20)800 = 40 · 30)630 = 21 · 50)556 = 11R6 · 11R3 · 60)720 = 12 · 204 · 30)524 = 17R14 · 21 · 20)346 = 17R6 · 120R6 · 17R14 · 40)859 = 21R19 · 40 · 7)846 = 120R6 · 3)612 = 204 · 4)420 = 105 · 11R30 · 105

Page 35

REVIEW: + − × Complete. Name_____

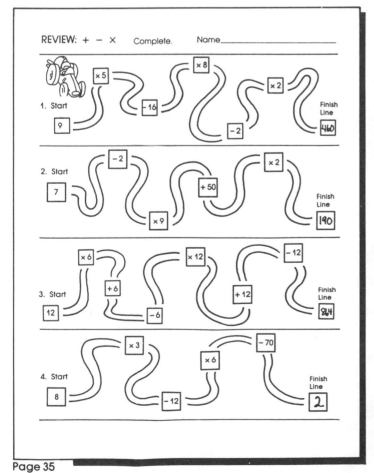

1. Start 9 ×5 −16 ×8 −2 ×2 Finish Line 460

2. Start 7 −2 ×9 +50 ×2 Finish Line 190

3. Start 12 ×6 +6 −6 ×12 +12 −12 Finish Line 84

4. Start 8 ×3 ×6 −12 −70 Finish Line 2

Page 36

BASIC REVIEW: × ÷ Name_____

Complete the number sentences.

8	×	3	×	2	=	48
÷		+		+		+
2	×	1	×	1	=	2
÷		+		+		+
2	×	3	×	2	=	12
=		=		=		=
2	×	1	×	1	=	2

4	×	2	×	4	=	32
÷		+		+		+
1	×	1	×	1	×	1
÷		+		+		+
4	×	2	×	1	=	8
=		=		=		=
1	×	1	×	4	=	4

6	×	2	×	3	=	36
÷		+		+		+
3	×	1	×	1	=	3
÷		+		+		+
2	×	1	×	3	=	6
=		=		=		=
1	×	2	×	1	=	2

5	×	8	×	2	=	80
÷		+		+		+
1	×	4	×	2	=	8
÷		+		+		+
5	×	2	×	1	=	10
=		=		=		=
1	×	1	×	1	=	1

Answer Key

Page 37

REVIEW: + − × ÷   Name_____

Start at the bottom of the steps. Write your answer at the top.

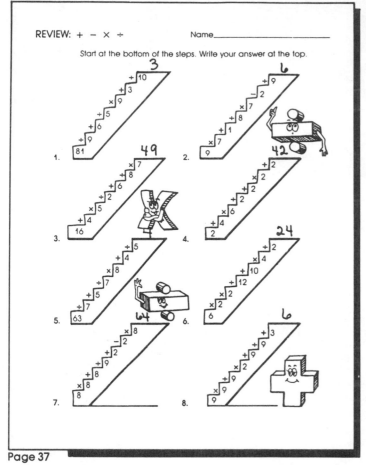

1. (answer: 3)
2. (answer: 6)
3. (answer: 49, 42)
4. (answer: 24)
5. (answer: 64)
6.
7.
8. (answer: 6)

Page 38

BASIC REVIEW: + − × ÷   Name_____

Work problems. Use answers to complete number crosses.

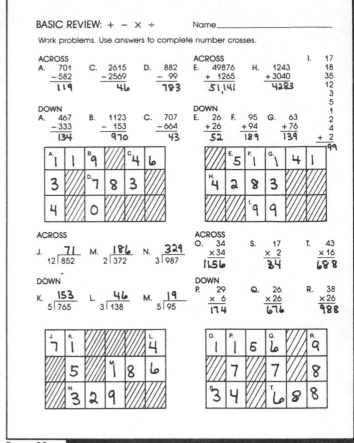

ACROSS
A. 701
   − 582
   —————
   119

C. 2615
   − 2569
   —————
   46

D. 882
   − 99
   —————
   783

E. 49876
   + 1265
   —————
   51,141

H. 1243
   + 3040
   —————
   4283

I. 17
   18
   35
   12
   3
   1
   2
   4
   + 2
   —————
   99

DOWN
A. 467
   − 333
   —————
   134

B. 1123
   − 153
   —————
   970

C. 707
   − 664
   —————
   43

E. 26
   + 26
   —————
   52

F. 95
   + 94
   —————
   189

G. 63
   + 76
   —————
   139

Number cross (top left): A. 1 1, B. 9, C. 4 6 / 3, D. 7 8 3 / 4, 0
Number cross (top right): E. 5 1 4 1 / H. 4 2 8 3 / I. 9 9

ACROSS
J. 71
   12⟌852

M. 186
   2⟌372

N. 329
   3⟌987

O. 34
   × 34
   —————
   1156

S. 17
   × 2
   —————
   34

T. 43
   × 16
   —————
   688

DOWN
K. 153
   5⟌765

L. 46
   3⟌138

M. 19
   5⟌95

P. 29
   × 6
   —————
   174

Q. 26
   × 26
   —————
   676

R. 38
   × 26
   —————
   988

Number cross (bottom left): J. 7 1, L. 4 / K. 5, M. 1 8 6 / N. 3 2 9
Number cross (bottom right): O. 1, P. 5, Q. 6, R. 9 / 7 7 8 / S. 3 4, T. 6 8 8

Page 39

MATH WORDS   Name_____

There are at least 30 words to seek and find.

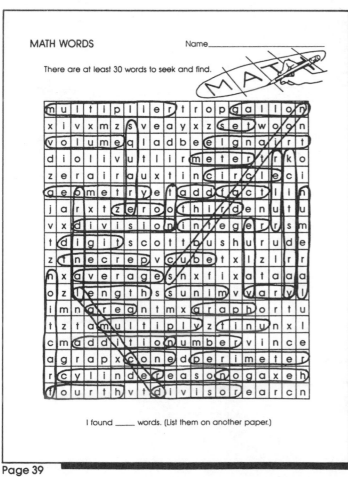

I found _____ words. (List them on another paper.)

Page 40

SUBTRACTION   Name_____

Use the decoder to find the secret message.

m	d	y	t	a	i	o	e	u
3257	2715	1318	4513	5878	1567	2079	1292	3401

9003
− 7685
—————
1318

8043
− 5964
—————
2079

8400
− 4999
—————
3401

7021
− 3764
—————
3257

6407
− 529
—————
5878

6700
− 3985
—————
2715

3400
− 2108
—————
1292

7004
− 5437
—————
1567

5308
− 795
—————
4513

YOU MADE IT!

Find the End Number.

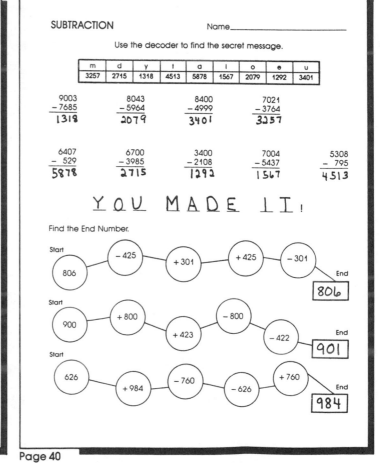

Start 806 → − 425 → + 301 → + 425 → − 301 → End 806

Start 900 → + 800 → + 423 → − 800 → − 422 → End 901

Start 626 → + 984 → − 760 → − 626 → + 760 → End 984

Answer Key

Page 41

CROSS NUMBER PUZZLE   Name_____

Across
1. 9 × 2
3. 320 + 8
6. 48 ÷ 4
7. 606 + 3
8. 50 − 4
11. 10 + 9
13. 864 ÷ 2
15. 7 × 6
16. 11 × 9
17. 3930 ÷ 10

Down
1. 5 × 3
2. 799 + 25
3. 8 × 4
4. 618 + 3
5. 574 + 7
9. 512 + 100
10. 2196 ÷ 4
12. 1353 ÷ 11
14. 7 × 5 + 4
15. 7 × 7

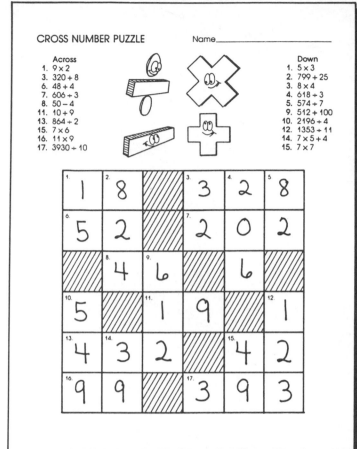

1. 1	2. 8	▨	3. 3	4. 2	5. 8
6. 5	2	▨	7. 2	0	2
▨	8. 4	9. 6	▨	6	▨
10. 5	▨	11. 1	9	▨	12. 1
13. 4	14. 3	2	▨	15. 4	2
16. 9	9	▨	17. 3	9	3

Page 41

Page 42

CROSS NUMBER PUZZLE   Name_____

1. 1	9	2. 2	6	▨	3. 3	7	1	1
2. 2	▨	4. 4	5	0	▨			
▨	6. 3	0	▨	6	▨	7. 1	8. 4	2
9. 7	▨	10. 9	0	4	▨	2		
12. 8	1	▨	9	▨	9	▨	13. 2	1	8
9	▨	14. 7	0	3	▨	15. 8	7	
16. 6	17. 5	2	0	▨	18. 2	3	19. 3	20. 3
▨	7	▨	21. 4	6	1	2	▨	0

Across
1. 321 × 6
3. 4010 − 299
4. 150 × 3
6. 750 ÷ 25
7. 23 + 57 + 62
10. 8136 ÷ 9
12. 9 × 9
13. 620 − 402
14. 4218 ÷ 6
15. 21 + 62 + 4
16. 1304 × 5
18. 69 ÷ 3
19. 9 × 5 + 18
21. 9593 − 4981

Down
1. 24 ÷ 2
2. 8 × 8
5. 80 × 7
8. 819 − 398
9. 5499 + 2397
10. 934 × 106
11. 7 × 7
13. 9 + 9 + 9
14. 8 × 9
15. 1104 − 272
17. 8 × 6 + 9
18. 126 ÷ 6
20. 300 ÷ 10

Page 42

Page 43

PARTS of a WHOLE   Name_____

Write the fraction for each drawing.

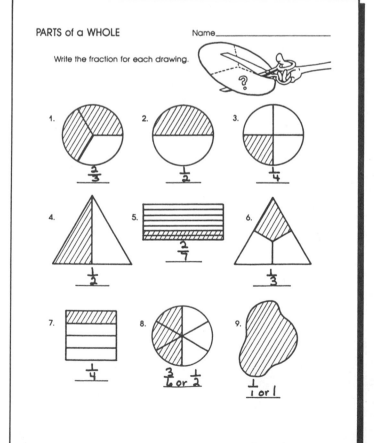

1. 2/3
2. 1/2
3. 1/4
4. 1/2
5. 2/7
6. 1/3
7. 1/4
8. 3/6 or 1/2
9. 1/1 or 1

Page 43

Page 44

FRACTIONS in LOWEST TERMS   Name_____

A fraction is in lowest terms when 1 is the only factor that divides both the numerator and denominator.
 1. Find the greatest common factor.
 2. Divide the numerator and the denominator by their greatest common factor.

$$\frac{8}{16} = \frac{1}{2} \qquad \frac{18}{24} = \frac{3}{4}$$

1. $\frac{6}{12} = \frac{1}{2}$
2. $\frac{24}{30} = \frac{4}{5}$
3. $\frac{9}{36} = \frac{1}{4}$
4. $\frac{15}{24} = \frac{5}{8}$

5. $\frac{9}{18} = \frac{1}{2}$
6. $\frac{12}{9} = \frac{4}{3}$
7. $\frac{5}{10} = \frac{1}{2}$
8. $\frac{24}{32} = \frac{3}{4}$

9. $\frac{10}{35} = \frac{2}{7}$
10. $\frac{18}{90} = \frac{1}{5}$
11. $\frac{8}{32} = \frac{1}{4}$
12. $\frac{18}{14} = \frac{9}{7}$

13. $\frac{2}{6} = \frac{1}{3}$
14. $\frac{12}{18} = \frac{2}{3}$
15. $\frac{24}{9} = \frac{8}{3}$

16. $\frac{7}{28} = \frac{1}{4}$
17. $\frac{6}{21} = \frac{2}{7}$

Page 44

Answer Key

ADDING FRACTIONS   Name_____

Shade each pie with the fraction.
Then, write the answer.

1. $\frac{1}{2}$ + $\frac{1}{2}$ = 1

2. $\frac{2}{3}$ + $\frac{2}{9}$ = $\frac{8}{9}$

3. $\frac{2}{5}$ + $\frac{1}{3}$ = $\frac{11}{15}$

4. $\frac{1}{2}$ + $\frac{2}{5}$ = $\frac{9}{10}$

5. $\frac{1}{3}$ + $\frac{1}{2}$ = $\frac{5}{6}$

RENAMING IMPROPER and MIXED FRACTIONS   Name_____

To rename $\frac{7}{6}$ as a mixed numeral, do step by step the following.

1. Divide numerator by denominator.
2. Write quotient as a whole number.
3. Write remainder over divisor.
4. Always reduce to lowest terms.

$\frac{7}{6} \rightarrow 6\overline{)7}\;\; \begin{array}{c}1R1\\-6\\\hline 1\end{array} = 1\frac{1}{6}$

1. $\frac{14}{3} = 4\frac{2}{3}$ 2. $\frac{29}{5} = 5\frac{4}{5}$ 3. $\frac{4}{3} = 1\frac{1}{3}$ 4. $\frac{11}{9} = 1\frac{2}{9}$

5. $\frac{7}{2} = 3\frac{1}{2}$ 6. $\frac{36}{8} = 4\frac{1}{2}$ 7. $\frac{18}{5} = 3\frac{3}{5}$ 8. $\frac{9}{5} = 1\frac{4}{5}$

To rename $1\frac{1}{2}$ as an improper fraction, study these steps.

1. Multiply the denominator by the whole number.
2. Add the numerator.
3. Write the sum over the denominator.

$1\frac{1}{2} \rightarrow \frac{(1 \times 2) + 1}{2} = \frac{3}{2}$

9. $5\frac{7}{10} = \frac{57}{10}$ 10. $2\frac{4}{12} = \frac{28}{12}$ 11. $5\frac{1}{3} = \frac{16}{3}$ 12. $7\frac{5}{8} = \frac{61}{8}$

13. $4\frac{3}{4} = \frac{19}{4}$ 14. $2\frac{5}{10} = \frac{25}{10}$ 15. $9\frac{1}{7} = \frac{64}{7}$

ADDITION - (Mixed Numerals)   Name_____

$$3\frac{1}{5} = 3\frac{2}{10}$$
$$+ 2\frac{7}{10} = 2\frac{7}{10}$$
$$\overline{\quad\quad 5\frac{9}{10}}$$

$$5\frac{1}{4} = 5\frac{3}{12}$$
$$+ 1\frac{1}{6} = 1\frac{2}{12}$$
$$\overline{\quad\quad 6\frac{5}{12}}$$

1. $8\frac{1}{3}$ + $7\frac{1}{4}$ = $15\frac{7}{12}$

2. $6\frac{3}{4}$ + $2\frac{1}{8}$ = $8\frac{7}{8}$

3. $9\frac{7}{10}$ + $8\frac{1}{15}$ = $17\frac{23}{30}$

4. $8\frac{7}{10}$ + $1\frac{1}{5}$ = $9\frac{9}{10}$

5. $5\frac{5}{6}$ + $3\frac{1}{12}$ = $8\frac{11}{12}$

6. $4\frac{1}{2}$ + $7\frac{1}{3}$ = $11\frac{5}{6}$

7. $5\frac{1}{2}$ + $2\frac{1}{3}$ = $7\frac{5}{6}$

8. $7\frac{1}{6}$ + $8\frac{1}{4}$ = $15\frac{5}{12}$

9. $5\frac{1}{3}$ + $3\frac{4}{9}$ = $8\frac{7}{9}$

10. $6\frac{1}{5}$ + $1\frac{7}{10}$ = $7\frac{9}{10}$

11. $1\frac{1}{7}$ + $5\frac{3}{7}$ = $6\frac{4}{7}$

12. $3\frac{1}{2}$ + $4\frac{1}{4}$ = $7\frac{3}{4}$

Challenge—
Solve the equations.

$3\frac{7}{8} + 1\frac{3}{4} = 5 + n$

$\frac{31}{8} + \frac{14}{8} = 5 + n$

$\frac{45}{8} = 5 + n$

$5\frac{5}{8} = 5 + \frac{5}{8}$

$n = \frac{5}{8}$

$15\frac{3}{8} + 29\frac{5}{6} = 45 + n$

$\frac{123}{8} + \frac{179}{6} = 45 + n$

$\frac{369}{24} + \frac{716}{24} = 45 + n$

$\frac{1085}{24} = 45 + n$

$45\frac{5}{24} = 45 + \frac{5}{24}$

$n = \frac{5}{24}$

SUBTRACTING FRACTIONS   Name_____

Example—
$$3\frac{1}{2} = 3\frac{3}{6}$$
$$- 2\frac{2}{6} = 2\frac{2}{6}$$
$$\overline{\quad\quad 1\frac{1}{6}}$$

Subtract. Show all work.

1. $3\frac{4}{7}$ − $1\frac{1}{14}$ = $2\frac{1}{2}$

2. $8\frac{5}{6}$ − $3\frac{3}{8}$ = $5\frac{11}{24}$

3. $7\frac{7}{8}$ − $2\frac{1}{4}$ = $5\frac{5}{8}$

4. $6\frac{1}{2}$ − $1\frac{5}{12}$ = $5\frac{1}{12}$

5. $7\frac{3}{8}$ − $6\frac{1}{6}$ = $1\frac{5}{24}$

6. $9\frac{1}{2}$ − $6\frac{1}{12}$ = $3\frac{5}{12}$

7. $8\frac{2}{3}$ − $4\frac{1}{6}$ = $4\frac{1}{2}$

8. $5\frac{1}{2}$ − $2\frac{1}{4}$ = $3\frac{1}{4}$

9. $9\frac{4}{5}$ − $1\frac{3}{10}$ = $8\frac{1}{2}$

10. $9\frac{2}{5}$ − $2\frac{4}{15}$ = $7\frac{2}{15}$

11. $6\frac{7}{12}$ − $1\frac{1}{2}$ = $5\frac{1}{12}$

12. $9\frac{1}{3}$ − $8\frac{1}{4}$ = $1\frac{1}{12}$

Answer Key

MULTIPLYING a FRACTION by a FRACTION

Name_____

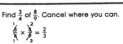

Find $\frac{3}{4}$ of $\frac{8}{9}$. Cancel where you can.

$$\frac{\cancel{8}^{2}}{\cancel{9}^{3}} \times \frac{\cancel{3}^{1}}{\cancel{4}^{1}} = \frac{2}{3}$$

Multiply numerators.
Multiply denominators.

1. $\frac{1}{4} \times \frac{3}{5} = \frac{3}{20}$
2. $\frac{8}{8} \times \frac{3}{\cancel{16}_2} = \frac{3}{16}$
3. $\frac{8}{1} \times \frac{2}{\cancel{24}} = \frac{2}{7}$
4. $\frac{1}{\cancel{4}} \times \frac{3}{\cancel{3}} = \frac{1}{4}$

5. $\frac{8}{\cancel{12}_3} \times \frac{2}{\cancel{18}_3} = \frac{2}{9}$
6. $\frac{8}{\cancel{9}} \times \frac{3}{\cancel{32}_4} = \frac{3}{4}$
7. $\frac{8}{\cancel{9}_3} \times \frac{1}{\cancel{8}_2} = \frac{1}{6}$
8. $\frac{4}{\cancel{9}_1} \times \frac{5}{\cancel{36}_9} = \frac{5}{9}$

9. $\frac{2}{9} \times \frac{\cancel{16}}{\cancel{18}_5} = \frac{2}{5}$
10. $\frac{8}{\cancel{9}_3} \times \frac{2}{\cancel{16}_3} = \frac{2}{9}$
11. $\frac{1}{\cancel{12}_4} \times \frac{3}{\cancel{28}_4} = \frac{3}{16}$
12. $\frac{8}{\cancel{9}_1} \times \frac{3}{\cancel{24}_8} = \frac{3}{8}$

13. $\frac{\cancel{39}}{\cancel{36}_9} \times \frac{5}{\cancel{13}_1} = \frac{1}{3}$
14. $\frac{3}{\cancel{36}_2} \times \frac{\cancel{18}}{\cancel{36}_5} = \frac{3}{10}$
15. $\frac{8}{\cancel{16}} \times \frac{3}{\cancel{48}_5} = \frac{3}{5}$
16. $\frac{1}{\cancel{21}_1} \times \frac{2}{\cancel{48}_7} = \frac{2}{7}$

17. $\frac{2}{1} \times \frac{3}{\cancel{24}_8} = \frac{3}{8}$
18. $\frac{8}{\cancel{9}} \times \frac{\cancel{28}}{\cancel{36}} = \frac{3}{7}$
19. $\frac{8}{\cancel{28}_2} \times \frac{1}{\cancel{8}} = \frac{1}{4}$
20. $\frac{4}{\cancel{9}_1} \times \frac{\cancel{24}}{\cancel{36}_8} = \frac{3}{8}$

Page 49

FRACTIONAL PARTS

Name_____

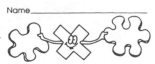

Multiply the problems in the puzzle.

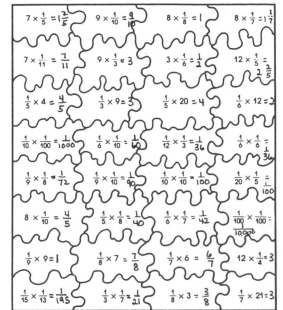

$7 \times \frac{1}{5} = 1\frac{2}{5}$	$9 \times \frac{1}{10} = \frac{9}{10}$	$8 \times \frac{1}{8} = 1$	$8 \times \frac{1}{7} = 1\frac{1}{7}$
$7 \times \frac{1}{11} = \frac{7}{11}$	$9 \times \frac{1}{3} = 3$	$3 \times \frac{1}{6} = \frac{1}{2}$	$12 \times \frac{1}{5} = 2\frac{2}{5}$
$\frac{1}{5} \times 4 = \frac{4}{5}$	$\frac{1}{3} \times 9 = 3$	$\frac{1}{5} \times 20 = 4$	$\frac{1}{6} \times 12 = 2$
$\frac{1}{10} \times \frac{1}{100} = \frac{1}{1000}$	$\frac{1}{6} \times \frac{1}{10} = \frac{1}{60}$	$\frac{1}{12} \times \frac{1}{3} = \frac{1}{36}$	$\frac{1}{6} \times \frac{1}{6} = \frac{1}{36}$
$\frac{1}{9} \times \frac{1}{8} = \frac{1}{72}$	$\frac{1}{9} \times \frac{1}{10} = \frac{1}{90}$	$\frac{1}{10} \times \frac{1}{10} = \frac{1}{100}$	$\frac{1}{20} \times \frac{1}{5} = \frac{1}{100}$
$8 \times \frac{1}{10} = \frac{4}{5}$	$\frac{1}{5} \times \frac{1}{8} = \frac{1}{40}$	$\frac{1}{6} \times \frac{1}{7} = \frac{1}{42}$	$\frac{1}{100} \times \frac{1}{100} = \frac{1}{10,000}$
$\frac{1}{9} \times 9 = 1$	$\frac{1}{8} \times 7 = \frac{7}{8}$	$\frac{1}{7} \times 6 = \frac{6}{7}$	$12 \times \frac{1}{4} = 3$
$\frac{1}{15} \times \frac{1}{13} = \frac{1}{195}$	$\frac{1}{3} \times \frac{1}{7} = \frac{1}{21}$	$\frac{1}{8} \times 3 = \frac{3}{8}$	$\frac{1}{7} \times 21 = 3$

Page 50

ADDING LIKE FRACTIONS

Name_____

Add problems to find the real gem. Shade in answer gems. The one left is the real gem.

$\frac{3}{8} + \frac{2}{8} = \frac{5}{8}$ $\frac{4}{7} + \frac{1}{7} = \frac{5}{7}$ $\frac{4}{6} + \frac{1}{6} = \frac{5}{6}$ $\frac{1}{3} + \frac{1}{3} = \frac{2}{3}$ $\frac{1}{4} + \frac{1}{4} = \frac{2}{4}$ $\frac{1}{8} + \frac{1}{8} = \frac{2}{8}$ $\frac{1}{6} + \frac{1}{6} = \frac{2}{6}$

$\frac{1}{8} + \frac{4}{8} = \frac{5}{8}$ $\frac{3}{20} + \frac{4}{20} = \frac{7}{20}$ $\frac{4}{10} + \frac{3}{10} = \frac{7}{10}$ $\frac{1}{5} + \frac{3}{5} = \frac{4}{5}$ $\frac{4}{12} + \frac{5}{12} = \frac{9}{12}$ $\frac{5}{15} + \frac{4}{15} = \frac{9}{15}$ $\frac{14}{20} + \frac{5}{20} = \frac{14}{20}$

$\frac{3}{16} + \frac{5}{16} = \frac{8}{16}$ $\frac{1}{8} + \frac{6}{8} = \frac{7}{8}$ $\frac{2}{5} + \frac{1}{5} = \frac{3}{5}$ $\frac{7}{12} + \frac{2}{12} = \frac{9}{12}$ $\frac{2}{13} + \frac{3}{13} = \frac{5}{13}$ $\frac{5}{17} + \frac{8}{17} = \frac{13}{17}$ $\frac{9}{18} + \frac{8}{18} = \frac{17}{18}$

$\frac{3}{15} + \frac{5}{15} = \frac{8}{15}$ $\frac{5}{12} + \frac{2}{12} = \frac{7}{12}$ $\frac{5}{14} + \frac{4}{14} = \frac{9}{14}$ $\frac{1}{7} + \frac{5}{7} = \frac{6}{7}$ $\frac{6}{16} + \frac{7}{16} = \frac{13}{16}$ $\frac{7}{21} + \frac{8}{21} = \frac{15}{21}$ $\frac{5}{10} + \frac{4}{10} = \frac{9}{10}$

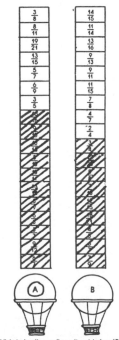

Page 51

ADDING 3 FRACTIONS

Name_____

Work problems. Shade in answers on balloon A or B height to see how high each balloon flew.

$\frac{1}{10} + \frac{4}{10} + \frac{3}{10} = \frac{8}{10}$ $\frac{1}{5} + \frac{2}{5} + \frac{1}{5} = \frac{4}{5}$ $\frac{1}{7} + \frac{1}{7} + \frac{1}{7} = \frac{3}{7}$ $\frac{4}{9} + \frac{1}{9} + \frac{2}{9} = \frac{7}{9}$

$\frac{1}{4} + \frac{1}{4} + \frac{1}{4} = \frac{3}{4}$ $\frac{1}{10} + \frac{5}{10} + \frac{1}{10} = \frac{9}{10}$ $\frac{3}{7} + \frac{2}{7} + \frac{1}{7} = \frac{6}{7}$ $\frac{2}{8} + \frac{1}{8} + \frac{2}{8} = \frac{5}{8}$

$\frac{3}{9} + \frac{3}{9} + \frac{2}{9} = \frac{8}{9}$ $\frac{5}{15} + \frac{3}{15} + \frac{4}{15} = \frac{12}{15}$ $\frac{1}{10} + \frac{5}{10} + \frac{1}{10} = \frac{7}{10}$ $\frac{5}{11} + \frac{1}{11} + \frac{4}{11} = \frac{10}{11}$

$\frac{3}{12} + \frac{5}{12} + \frac{1}{12} = \frac{9}{12}$ $\frac{4}{7} + \frac{1}{7} + \frac{1}{7} = \frac{6}{7}$ $\frac{7}{14} + \frac{2}{14} + \frac{4}{14} = \frac{13}{14}$ $\frac{7}{20} + \frac{2}{20} + \frac{4}{20} = \frac{12}{20}$

$\frac{3}{8} + \frac{2}{8} + \frac{1}{8} = \frac{6}{8}$ $\frac{9}{21} + \frac{5}{21} + \frac{4}{21} = \frac{18}{21}$ $\frac{2}{13} + \frac{1}{13} + \frac{7}{13} = \frac{10}{13}$ $\frac{7}{16} + \frac{3}{16} + \frac{5}{16} = \frac{15}{16}$

Which balloon flew the highest?

Page 52

Answer Key

FRACTIONS: LOWEST TERMS

Name_____

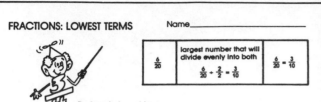

| $\frac{6}{20}$ | largest number that will divide evenly into both $\frac{6}{20} \div \frac{2}{2} = \frac{3}{10}$ | $\frac{6}{20} = \frac{3}{10}$ |

Reduce to lowest terms.

$\frac{5}{20} = \frac{1}{4}$ $\frac{8}{20} = \frac{2}{5}$ $\frac{3}{15} = \frac{1}{5}$ $\frac{12}{20} = \frac{3}{5}$

$\frac{2}{8} = \frac{1}{4}$ $\frac{12}{16} = \frac{3}{4}$ $\frac{14}{16} = \frac{7}{8}$ $\frac{4}{8} = \frac{1}{2}$

$\frac{9}{12} = \frac{3}{4}$ $\frac{5}{10} = \frac{1}{2}$ $\frac{6}{10} = \frac{3}{5}$ $\frac{10}{15} = \frac{2}{3}$

$\frac{2}{4} = \frac{1}{2}$ $\frac{4}{8} = \frac{1}{2}$ $\frac{6}{24} = \frac{1}{4}$ $\frac{6}{8} = \frac{3}{4}$

$\frac{8}{16} = \frac{1}{2}$ $\frac{2}{12} = \frac{1}{6}$ $\frac{2}{10} = \frac{1}{5}$ $\frac{8}{12} = \frac{2}{3}$

$\frac{4}{20} = \frac{1}{5}$ $\frac{3}{12} = \frac{1}{4}$ $\frac{9}{15} = \frac{3}{5}$ $\frac{4}{12} = \frac{1}{3}$

$\frac{10}{24} = \frac{5}{12}$ $\frac{6}{20} = \frac{3}{10}$ $\frac{10}{12} = \frac{5}{6}$ $\frac{12}{24} = \frac{1}{2}$

$\frac{4}{10} = \frac{2}{5}$ $\frac{8}{10} = \frac{4}{5}$ $\frac{2}{10} = \frac{1}{5}$ $\frac{6}{12} = \frac{1}{2}$

Page 53

EQUIVALENT FRACTIONS

Name_____

Match the pairs of equivalent fractions.

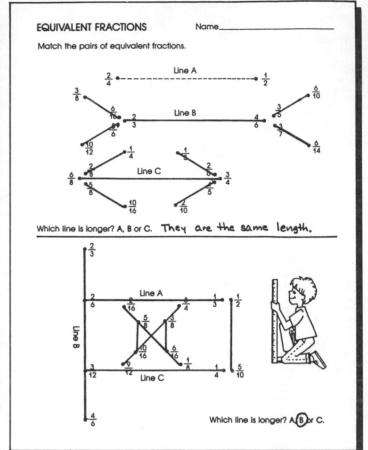

Which line is longer? A, B or C. They are the same length.

Which line is longer? A, (B) or C.

Page 54

FRACTIONS: IMPROPER TO MIXED

Change fractions to mixed numbers. Shade in each answer to find the path to the pot of gold.

1. $\frac{11}{9} = 1\frac{2}{9}$ 2. $\frac{8}{3} = 2\frac{2}{3}$ 3. $\frac{8}{7} = 1\frac{1}{7}$ 4. $\frac{11}{6} = 1\frac{5}{6}$

5. $\frac{7}{3} = 2\frac{1}{3}$ 6. $\frac{7}{6} = 1\frac{1}{6}$ 7. $\frac{9}{4} = 2\frac{1}{4}$ 8. $\frac{8}{5} = 1\frac{3}{5}$

9. $\frac{4}{3} = 1\frac{1}{3}$ 10. $\frac{7}{2} = 3\frac{1}{2}$ 11. $\frac{3}{2} = 1\frac{1}{2}$ 12. $\frac{6}{5} = 1\frac{1}{5}$

13. $\frac{7}{4} = 1\frac{3}{4}$ 14. $\frac{9}{2} = 4\frac{1}{2}$ 15. $\frac{11}{8} = 1\frac{3}{8}$ 16. $\frac{5}{2} = 2\frac{1}{2}$

17. $\frac{9}{7} = 1\frac{2}{7}$ 18. $\frac{11}{4} = 2\frac{3}{4}$ 19. $\frac{17}{12} = 1\frac{5}{12}$ 20. $\frac{13}{12} = 1\frac{1}{12}$

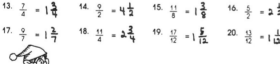

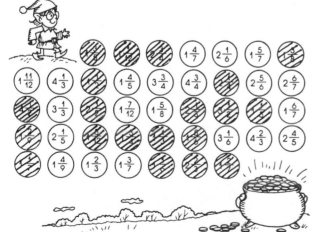

Page 55

FRACTIONS: MIXED TO IMPROPER

Name_____

Work problems. Connect dots in the order of the answers

1. $1\frac{2}{5} = \frac{7}{5}$ 2. $1\frac{1}{3} = \frac{4}{3}$

3. $1\frac{5}{7} = \frac{12}{7}$ 4. $2\frac{2}{3} = \frac{8}{3}$

5. $2\frac{5}{8} = \frac{21}{8}$ 6. $2\frac{1}{2} = \frac{5}{2}$

7. $1\frac{5}{6} = \frac{11}{6}$ 8. $1\frac{1}{5} = \frac{6}{5}$

9. $2\frac{4}{5} = \frac{14}{5}$ 10. $1\frac{1}{16} = \frac{17}{16}$

11. $1\frac{1}{2} = \frac{3}{2}$ 12. $3\frac{1}{5} = \frac{16}{5}$

13. $1\frac{11}{12} = \frac{23}{12}$ 14. $1\frac{7}{8} = \frac{15}{8}$

15. $1\frac{6}{7} = \frac{13}{7}$ 16. $2\frac{1}{4} = \frac{9}{4}$

17. $1\frac{7}{12} = \frac{19}{12}$ 18. $1\frac{3}{7} = \frac{10}{7}$

19. $6\frac{2}{3} = \frac{20}{3}$ 20. $3\frac{3}{5} = \frac{18}{5}$

21. $1\frac{5}{21} = \frac{26}{21}$ 22. $1\frac{7}{36} = \frac{43}{36}$

23. $1\frac{9}{20} = \frac{29}{20}$ 24. $1\frac{13}{24} = \frac{37}{24}$

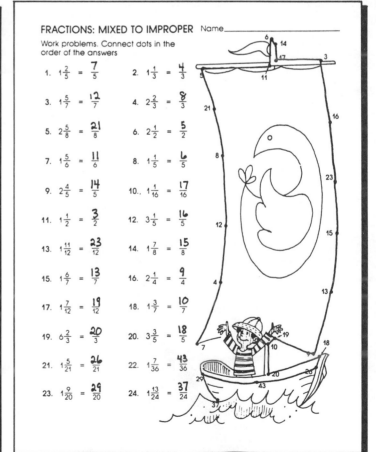

Page 56

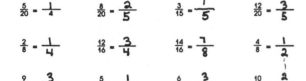

Math IF8744   116   © 1990 Instructional Fair, Inc.

Answer Key

Page 57

ADDING UNLIKE FRACTIONS — Name _____

Work problems. Shade in answers on pizzas to show which pieces have been eaten.

$\frac{1}{10} + \frac{4}{5} = \frac{9}{10}$ $\frac{3}{12} + \frac{1}{6} = \frac{5}{12}$ $\frac{1}{2} + \frac{1}{3} = \frac{5}{6}$ $\frac{3}{4} + \frac{1}{5} = \frac{19}{20}$ $\frac{1}{5} + \frac{1}{3} = \frac{8}{15}$

$\frac{2}{3} + \frac{1}{4} = \frac{11}{12}$ $\frac{2}{12} + \frac{9}{20} = \frac{7}{12}$ $\frac{2}{5} + \frac{9}{20} = \frac{17}{20}$ $\frac{1}{3} + \frac{2}{9} = \frac{5}{9}$ $\frac{3}{5} + \frac{1}{10} = \frac{7}{10}$

$\frac{1}{4} + \frac{1}{2} = \frac{3}{4}$ $\frac{1}{8} + \frac{1}{4} = \frac{3}{8}$ $\frac{1}{10} + \frac{1}{5} = \frac{3}{10}$ $\frac{2}{3} + \frac{1}{5} = \frac{13}{15}$ $\frac{1}{8} + \frac{1}{3} = \frac{11}{24}$

$\frac{1}{4} + \frac{1}{5} = \frac{9}{20}$ $\frac{3}{8} + \frac{1}{8} = \frac{23}{40}$ $\frac{9}{16} + \frac{3}{8} = \frac{15}{16}$ $\frac{2}{8} + \frac{1}{16} = \frac{13}{16}$ $\frac{1}{5} + \frac{1}{9} = \frac{14}{45}$

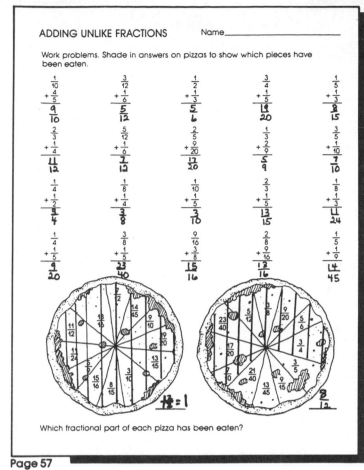

Which fractional part of each pizza has been eaten?

$\frac{12}{12} = 1$ $\frac{8}{12}$

Page 58

ADDING UNLIKE FRACTIONS — Name _____

Work problems. Use answers to guide coloring of stained glass window. Reduce fractions to lowest terms.

red $52\frac{4}{9} + 8\frac{7}{8} = 61\frac{23}{72}$ **blue** $16\frac{2}{7} + 14\frac{1}{3} = 30\frac{13}{21}$ **green** $40\frac{1}{2} + 50\frac{2}{3} = 91\frac{1}{6}$

orange $36\frac{5}{6} + 57\frac{1}{2} = 94\frac{1}{3}$ **blue** $39\frac{3}{4} + 54\frac{5}{8} = 94\frac{3}{8}$ **red** $72\frac{3}{4} + 67\frac{5}{8} = 140\frac{3}{8}$

yellow $84\frac{5}{6} + 94\frac{2}{3} = 179\frac{1}{2}$ **orange** $35\frac{7}{8} + 36\frac{1}{2} = 72\frac{3}{8}$ **purple** $4\frac{3}{8} + 3\frac{3}{4} = 8\frac{1}{8}$

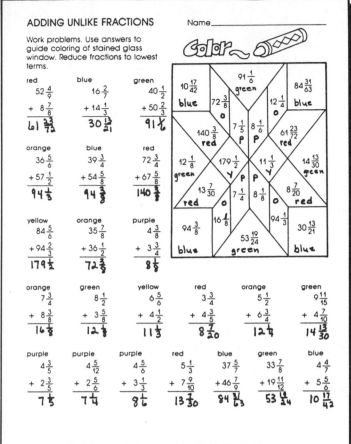

orange $7\frac{3}{4} + 8\frac{3}{8} = 16\frac{1}{8}$ **green** $8\frac{1}{2} + 3\frac{5}{8} = 12\frac{1}{8}$ **yellow** $6\frac{5}{6} + 4\frac{1}{2} = 11\frac{1}{3}$ **red** $3\frac{3}{4} + 4\frac{3}{5} = 8\frac{7}{20}$ **orange** $5\frac{1}{2} + 6\frac{3}{4} = 12\frac{1}{4}$ **green** $9\frac{11}{15} + 4\frac{7}{10} = 14\frac{13}{30}$

purple $4\frac{3}{5} + 2\frac{3}{5} = 7\frac{1}{5}$ **purple** $4\frac{5}{12} + 2\frac{5}{6} = 7\frac{1}{4}$ **purple** $4\frac{5}{6} + 3\frac{1}{3} = 8\frac{1}{6}$ **red** $5\frac{1}{3} + 7\frac{9}{10} = 13\frac{7}{30}$ **blue** $37\frac{5}{7} + 46\frac{7}{9} = 84\frac{31}{63}$ **green** $33\frac{7}{8} + 19\frac{11}{12} = 53\frac{19}{24}$ **blue** $4\frac{4}{7} + 5\frac{5}{6} = 10\frac{17}{42}$

Page 59

SUBTRACTING FRACTIONS — Name _____

Work problems. Where you find an answer, put an X. Where you don't, put an O.

$1\frac{1}{9} - \frac{7}{9} = \frac{3}{9}$ $1\frac{1}{4} - \frac{3}{4} = \frac{2}{4}$ $1\frac{1}{8} - \frac{5}{8} = \frac{4}{8}$ $1\frac{2}{5} - \frac{4}{5} = \frac{3}{5}$

$1\frac{1}{3} - \frac{2}{3} = \frac{2}{3}$ $1\frac{1}{12} - \frac{5}{12} = \frac{8}{12}$ $1\frac{1}{7} - \frac{6}{7} = \frac{2}{7}$ $1\frac{1}{5} - \frac{4}{5} = \frac{2}{5}$

$1\frac{1}{6} - \frac{5}{6} = \frac{2}{6}$ $1\frac{1}{8} - \frac{7}{8} = \frac{2}{8}$ $1\frac{5}{12} - \frac{7}{12} = \frac{10}{12}$ $1\frac{1}{12} - \frac{4}{12} = \frac{9}{12}$

$1\frac{1}{8} - \frac{1}{2} = \frac{5}{8}$ $1\frac{1}{8} - \frac{3}{4} = \frac{3}{8}$ $1\frac{5}{8} - \frac{3}{4} = \frac{7}{8}$ $1\frac{1}{10} - \frac{7}{10} = \frac{4}{10}$

$1\frac{1}{5} - \frac{1}{4} = \frac{19}{20}$ $1\frac{1}{8} - \frac{2}{3} = \frac{11}{24}$ $1\frac{1}{2} - \frac{3}{4} = \frac{3}{4}$ $1\frac{1}{3} - \frac{6}{7} = \frac{10}{21}$

$1\frac{1}{5} - \frac{3}{8} = \frac{33}{40}$ $1\frac{4}{5} - \frac{9}{10} = \frac{9}{10}$

$1\frac{1}{4} - \frac{3}{5} = \frac{13}{20}$ $1\frac{1}{3} - \frac{4}{5} = \frac{8}{15}$

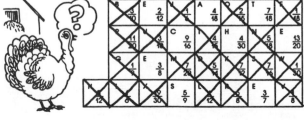

Page 60

SUBTRACTING UNLIKE FRACTIONS — Name _____

Work problems to solve riddle. Cross out answers to find out what letters are left.

$\frac{1}{2} - \frac{1}{5} = \frac{3}{10}$ $\frac{1}{3} - \frac{1}{4} = \frac{1}{12}$ $\frac{1}{3} - \frac{1}{6} = \frac{1}{6}$ $\frac{2}{3} - \frac{2}{5} = \frac{4}{15}$ $\frac{5}{9} - \frac{1}{2} = \frac{1}{18}$

$\frac{2}{3} - \frac{1}{2} = \frac{1}{6}$ $\frac{4}{5} - \frac{1}{6} = \frac{19}{30}$ $\frac{4}{5} - \frac{3}{10} = \frac{1}{2}$ $\frac{3}{4} - \frac{1}{3} = \frac{5}{12}$ $\frac{1}{3} - \frac{1}{5} = \frac{2}{15}$

$\frac{4}{5} - \frac{1}{4} = \frac{11}{20}$ $\frac{11}{12} - \frac{1}{3} = \frac{7}{12}$ $\frac{3}{4} - \frac{2}{5} = \frac{7}{20}$ $\frac{1}{3} - \frac{2}{9} = \frac{1}{9}$ $\frac{7}{8} - \frac{2}{7} = \frac{9}{14}$

$\frac{5}{8} - \frac{1}{2} = \frac{1}{8}$ $\frac{11}{16} - \frac{4}{16} = \frac{7}{16}$ $\frac{5}{6} - \frac{4}{5} = \frac{1}{30}$ $\frac{13}{18} - \frac{4}{9} = \frac{5}{18}$ $\frac{9}{14} - \frac{2}{7} = \frac{5}{14}$

What did the turkey say at Thanksgiving? _Eat cheese!_

Answer Key

Page 61

SUBTRACTING UNLIKE FRACTIONS   Name_____

Work problems.
Use answers to decode and say GREAT in . . .

 French
 Chinese

D I N G   H O W
$2\frac{9}{10}$ $4\frac{3}{8}$ $4\frac{9}{20}$ $1\frac{5}{8}$ $28\frac{7}{9}$ $1\frac{1}{2}$ $9\frac{3}{8}$

T R E S
$1\frac{7}{10}$ $1\frac{29}{40}$ $4\frac{5}{8}$ $9\frac{19}{70}$

B I E N
$17\frac{9}{16}$ $41\frac{37}{50}$ $2\frac{3}{4}$ $3\frac{13}{15}$

S U B   A R A S H L L   Japanese
$2\frac{7}{8}$ $5\frac{7}{12}$ $4\frac{3}{4}$ $1\frac{15}{16}$ $7\frac{3}{5}$ $5\frac{7}{12}$ $11\frac{3}{2}$ $2\frac{3}{4}$ $35\frac{25}{28}$ $4\frac{15}{28}$

S. $21\frac{7}{10}$
$-12\frac{3}{7}$
$9\frac{19}{70}$

H. $76\frac{4}{9}$
$-47\frac{2}{3}$
$28\frac{7}{9}$

D. $5\frac{1}{5}$
$-2\frac{3}{10}$
$2\frac{9}{10}$

A. $4\frac{1}{8}$
$-2\frac{3}{16}$
$1\frac{15}{16}$

W. $10\frac{1}{8}$
$-\frac{3}{4}$
$9\frac{3}{8}$

L. $59\frac{3}{4}$
$-23\frac{6}{7}$
$35\frac{25}{28}$

S. $12\frac{1}{3}$
$-\frac{5}{6}$
$11\frac{1}{2}$

E. $6\frac{2}{3}$
$-1\frac{5}{6}$
$4\frac{5}{6}$

I. $5\frac{1}{4}$
$-\frac{7}{8}$
$4\frac{3}{8}$

N. $7\frac{2}{3}$
$-3\frac{4}{5}$
$3\frac{13}{15}$

N. $16\frac{7}{10}$
$-12\frac{1}{4}$
$4\frac{9}{20}$

R. $8\frac{3}{5}$
$-6\frac{7}{8}$
$1\frac{29}{40}$

G. $3\frac{1}{2}$
$-1\frac{7}{8}$
$1\frac{5}{8}$

L. $7\frac{2}{7}$
$-2\frac{3}{4}$
$4\frac{15}{28}$

H. $6\frac{1}{2}$
$-2\frac{3}{4}$
$3\frac{3}{4}$

B. $71\frac{5}{16}$
$-53\frac{3}{4}$
$17\frac{9}{16}$

S. $7\frac{1}{4}$
$-4\frac{3}{8}$
$2\frac{7}{8}$

A. $5\frac{1}{4}$
$-1\frac{1}{2}$
$3\frac{7}{12}$

E. $7\frac{1}{4}$
$-4\frac{1}{2}$
$2\frac{3}{4}$

B. $12\frac{1}{2}$
$-7\frac{3}{4}$
$4\frac{3}{4}$

I. $83\frac{2}{7}$
$-41\frac{5}{8}$
$41\frac{37}{56}$

O. $8\frac{1}{3}$
$-6\frac{5}{8}$
$1\frac{1}{2}$

T. $7\frac{3}{10}$
$-5\frac{3}{8}$
$1\frac{7}{10}$

U. $14\frac{1}{3}$
$-8\frac{3}{4}$
$5\frac{2}{12}$

R. $16\frac{1}{10}$
$-8\frac{1}{2}$
$7\frac{3}{5}$

Page 61

Page 62

EQUIVALENT FRACTIONS   Name_____

Connect the equivalent fractions to complete the picture.

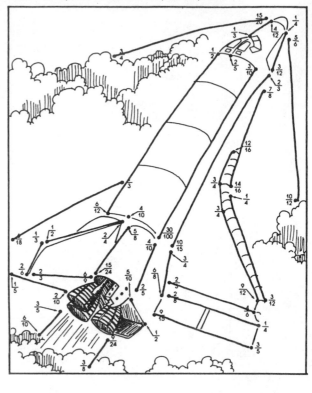
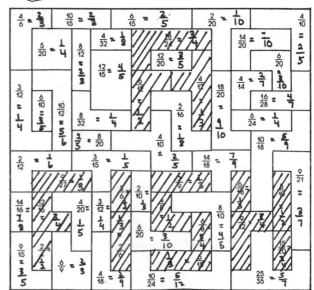

Page 62

Page 63

FRACTION REVIEW: + −   Name_____

Work each problem. Write answer in square.

a. $\frac{1}{4}+\frac{1}{6}=\frac{5}{12}$ e. $\frac{1}{3}+\frac{1}{6}=\frac{1}{2}$

b. $\frac{1}{2}+\frac{1}{3}=\frac{5}{6}$ f. $\frac{1}{6}+\frac{1}{2}=\frac{2}{3}$

c. $\frac{1}{2}-\frac{1}{4}=\frac{1}{4}$ g. $\frac{5}{6}-\frac{1}{12}=\frac{3}{4}$

d. $\frac{1}{2}-\frac{1}{6}=\frac{1}{3}$ h. $\frac{1}{2}-\frac{1}{3}=\frac{1}{6}$

i. $\frac{1}{4}+\frac{1}{3}=\frac{7}{12}$

Add every row, every column and both diagonals. If your answers are correct, all totals will be the same.

a. $\frac{5}{12}$	b. $\frac{5}{12}$	c. $\frac{1}{4}$	$\frac{18}{12}$
d. $\frac{1}{3}$	e. $\frac{1}{3}$	f. $\frac{2}{3}$	$\frac{1}{6}$
g. $\frac{3}{4}$	h. $\frac{1}{6}$	i. $\frac{7}{12}$	$\frac{18}{12}$
$\frac{18}{12}$	$\frac{9}{6}$	$\frac{18}{12}$	$4\frac{1}{2}$

Complete the table.

+	$\frac{1}{8}$	$\frac{1}{3}$	$\frac{1}{6}$	$\frac{5}{8}$	$\frac{1}{5}$
$\frac{1}{4}$	$\frac{3}{8}$	$\frac{7}{12}$	$\frac{5}{12}$	$\frac{7}{8}$	$\frac{9}{20}$
$\frac{1}{5}$	$\frac{13}{40}$	$\frac{8}{15}$	$\frac{11}{30}$	$\frac{33}{40}$	$\frac{2}{5}$
$\frac{1}{3}$	$\frac{11}{24}$	$\frac{2}{3}$	$\frac{1}{2}$	$\frac{23}{24}$	$\frac{8}{5}$
$\frac{1}{8}$	$\frac{1}{4}$	$\frac{11}{24}$	$\frac{7}{24}$	$\frac{3}{4}$	$\frac{13}{40}$
$\frac{1}{6}$	$\frac{7}{24}$	$\frac{1}{2}$	$\frac{1}{3}$	$\frac{19}{24}$	$\frac{11}{30}$

Complete these tables.

+	$\frac{1}{2}$	$\frac{1}{3}$	$\frac{1}{4}$	$\frac{1}{5}$	$\frac{1}{6}$
$\frac{1}{8}$	$\frac{5}{8}$	$\frac{11}{24}$	$\frac{3}{8}$	$\frac{13}{40}$	$\frac{7}{24}$

+	$\frac{1}{2}$	$\frac{1}{3}$	$\frac{1}{4}$	$\frac{1}{5}$	$\frac{1}{6}$
$\frac{1}{12}$	$\frac{7}{12}$	$\frac{5}{12}$	$\frac{1}{3}$	$\frac{17}{60}$	$\frac{1}{4}$

Page 63

Page 64

FRACTION REVIEW   Name_____

Reduce to lowest terms. Shade each part that is equivalent to $\frac{1}{2}$, $\frac{1}{3}$ or $\frac{3}{4}$.

What travels in all directions, yet is neither in the air nor on the ground?

A FISH

Page 64

Answer Key

Page 65

MULTIPLYING FRACTIONS   Name_____

Work problems. Use code to color the design B-blue, Y-yellow, O-orange, G-green.

$\frac{5}{6} \times \frac{3}{4} = \frac{5}{8}$ B $\frac{7}{10} \times \frac{3}{5} = \frac{21}{50}$ Y $\frac{2}{3} \times \frac{7}{8} = \frac{7}{12}$ G $\frac{3}{4} \times \frac{3}{5} = \frac{9}{20}$ O

$\frac{5}{6} \times \frac{4}{5} = \frac{2}{3}$ Y $\frac{3}{8} \times \frac{8}{10} = \frac{3}{10}$ Y $\frac{9}{16} \times \frac{5}{6} = \frac{15}{32}$ O $\frac{4}{7} \times \frac{1}{6} = \frac{2}{21}$ G

$\frac{5}{9} \times \frac{3}{5} = \frac{1}{3}$ Y $\frac{7}{12} \times \frac{5}{6} = \frac{35}{72}$ B $\frac{2}{5} \times \frac{1}{3} = \frac{2}{15}$ B $\frac{9}{10} \times \frac{2}{3} = \frac{3}{5}$ Y

$\frac{5}{8} \times \frac{3}{5} = \frac{3}{8}$ B $\frac{1}{3} \times \frac{4}{5} = \frac{4}{15}$ Y $\frac{3}{4} \times \frac{5}{8} = \frac{15}{32}$ O $\frac{5}{6} \times \frac{3}{8} = \frac{5}{16}$ B

$\frac{2}{5} \times \frac{5}{8} = \frac{1}{4}$ Y $\frac{5}{6} \times \frac{1}{3} = \frac{5}{18}$ O $\frac{7}{9} \times \frac{1}{4} = \frac{7}{36}$ O $\frac{3}{8} \times \frac{5}{12} = \frac{5}{32}$ B

$\frac{3}{7} \times \frac{14}{15} = \frac{2}{5}$ G $\frac{3}{4} \times \frac{2}{3} = \frac{1}{2}$ B $\frac{2}{7} \times \frac{3}{7} = \frac{6}{49}$ B $\frac{5}{6} \times \frac{1}{10} = \frac{1}{12}$ Y

$\frac{2}{3} \times \frac{4}{5} = \frac{8}{15}$ O $\frac{7}{10} \times \frac{5}{8} = \frac{7}{16}$ O $\frac{1}{6} \times \frac{5}{6} = \frac{5}{36}$ B $\frac{3}{4} \times \frac{4}{5} = \frac{3}{5}$ B

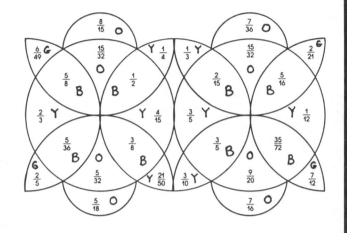

Page 66

MULTIPLYING FRACTIONS   Name_____

Complete these tables.

X	$\frac{3}{5}$	$\frac{1}{2}$	$\frac{2}{3}$	$\frac{1}{6}$	$\frac{1}{8}$
$\frac{1}{2}$	$\frac{3}{10}$	$\frac{1}{4}$	$\frac{2}{6}$	$\frac{1}{12}$	$\frac{1}{16}$
$\frac{3}{8}$	$\frac{9}{40}$	$\frac{3}{16}$	$\frac{1}{4}$	$\frac{1}{16}$	$\frac{3}{64}$
$\frac{4}{7}$	$\frac{12}{35}$	$\frac{2}{7}$	$\frac{8}{21}$	$\frac{2}{21}$	$\frac{1}{14}$
$\frac{5}{8}$	$\frac{3}{8}$	$\frac{5}{16}$	$\frac{5}{12}$	$\frac{5}{48}$	$\frac{5}{64}$
$\frac{1}{10}$	$\frac{3}{50}$	$\frac{1}{20}$	$\frac{2}{30}$	$\frac{1}{60}$	$\frac{1}{80}$

X	$\frac{1}{2}$	$\frac{3}{4}$	$\frac{1}{6}$	$\frac{3}{8}$	$\frac{1}{3}$
$\frac{1}{4}$	$\frac{1}{8}$	$\frac{3}{16}$	$\frac{1}{24}$	$\frac{3}{32}$	$\frac{1}{12}$
$\frac{1}{8}$	$\frac{1}{16}$	$\frac{3}{32}$	$\frac{1}{48}$	$\frac{3}{64}$	$\frac{1}{24}$
$\frac{1}{5}$	$\frac{1}{10}$	$\frac{3}{20}$	$\frac{1}{30}$	$\frac{3}{40}$	$\frac{1}{15}$
$\frac{2}{7}$	$\frac{1}{7}$	$\frac{3}{14}$	$\frac{1}{21}$	$\frac{3}{28}$	$\frac{2}{21}$
$\frac{1}{3}$	$\frac{1}{6}$	$\frac{1}{4}$	$\frac{1}{18}$	$\frac{1}{8}$	$\frac{1}{9}$

Page 67

MULTIPLYING with MIXED NUMBERS   Name_____

Change mixed numbers to improper fractions before multiplying.

$$300 \times 3\frac{1}{4}$$

$$\frac{\overset{75}{\cancel{300}}}{1} \times \frac{13}{\cancel{4}_1} = \frac{975}{1} = 975$$

1. $5\frac{1}{4} \times 3\frac{1}{5}$
$\frac{21}{4} \times \frac{16}{5} = \frac{84}{5}$
$\frac{84}{5} = 16\frac{4}{5}$

2. $2\frac{1}{3} \times 2\frac{1}{4}$
$\frac{7}{3} \times \frac{9}{4} = \frac{21}{4}$
$\frac{21}{4} = 5\frac{1}{4}$

3. $1\frac{1}{9} \times 3\frac{3}{5}$
$\frac{10}{9} \times \frac{18}{5}$
4

4. $2\frac{5}{8} \times 5\frac{1}{3}$
$\frac{21}{8} \times \frac{16}{3}$
14

5. $2\frac{6}{7} \times 5\frac{1}{4}$
$\frac{20}{7} \times \frac{21}{4}$
15

6. $3\frac{3}{4} \times 1\frac{3}{5}$
$\frac{15}{4} \times \frac{8}{5}$
6

7. $3\frac{2}{3} \times 2\frac{1}{7}$
$\frac{11}{3} \times \frac{15}{7} = \frac{55}{7}$
$\frac{55}{7} = 7\frac{6}{7}$

8. $4\frac{1}{6} \times 3\frac{3}{5}$
$\frac{25}{6} \times \frac{18}{5}$
15

9. $6\frac{2}{5} \times 3\frac{1}{8}$
$\frac{32}{5} \times \frac{25}{8}$
20

10. $1\frac{1}{7} \times 2\frac{5}{8}$
$\frac{8}{7} \times \frac{21}{8}$
3

11. $6\frac{3}{8} \times 1\frac{1}{9}$
$\frac{17}{8} \times \frac{10}{9} = \frac{85}{12}$
$\frac{85}{12} = 7\frac{1}{12}$

12. $3\frac{3}{4} \times \frac{2}{3}$
$\frac{15}{4} \times \frac{2}{3} = \frac{5}{2}$
$\frac{5}{2} = 2\frac{1}{2}$

13. $1\frac{1}{9} \times \frac{3}{4}$
$\frac{10}{9} \times \frac{3}{4}$
$\frac{5}{6}$

14. $3\frac{3}{8} \times 5\frac{1}{3}$
$\frac{27}{8} \times \frac{16}{3}$
18

15. $5\frac{1}{4} \times \frac{9}{20}$
$\frac{21}{4} \times \frac{9}{20} = \frac{12}{5}$
$\frac{12}{5} = 2\frac{2}{5}$

16. $2\frac{1}{4} \times \frac{4}{9}$
$\frac{9}{4} \times \frac{4}{9}$
1

Page 68

MULTIPLYING FRACTIONS   Name_____

Work problems. Find answer and circle letter. Write letters in order for message.

$2\frac{2}{3} \times \frac{3}{4}$	=	$2\frac{1}{4}$ A	2	(S)	
$4\frac{2}{3} \times 5\frac{1}{4}$	=	$24\frac{1}{3}$ B	$24\frac{1}{2}$	(U)	
$3\frac{3}{4} \times 5\frac{7}{9}$	=	$21\frac{2}{3}$ (P)	$21\frac{1}{3}$	C	
$6\frac{2}{5} \times 2\frac{1}{2}$	=	$15\frac{1}{2}$ D	16	(E)	
$5\frac{1}{5} \times 3\frac{1}{2}$	=	$18\frac{1}{5}$ (R)	$18\frac{2}{5}$	F	
$3\frac{1}{2} \times 3\frac{3}{4}$	=	$13\frac{1}{8}$ (N)	$13\frac{3}{8}$	H	
$5\frac{5}{9} \times 5\frac{1}{4}$	=	$29\frac{5}{6}$ G	$29\frac{1}{6}$	(O)	
$4\frac{5}{8} \times 2\frac{4}{5}$	=	$12\frac{19}{20}$ (W)	$12\frac{17}{20}$	J	
$5\frac{4}{7} \times 4\frac{1}{5}$	=	$23\frac{1}{5}$ I	$23\frac{2}{5}$	(Y)	
$5\frac{3}{4} \times \frac{4}{5}$	=	$4\frac{3}{5}$ (O)	$4\frac{1}{5}$	L	
$3\frac{3}{4} \times 2\frac{1}{6}$	=	$8\frac{3}{8}$ K	$8\frac{1}{8}$	(U)	
$5\frac{2}{3} \times 7\frac{4}{5}$	=	$44\frac{2}{3}$ M	$44\frac{1}{5}$	(O)	
$4\frac{1}{2} \times 2\frac{5}{8}$	=	$11\frac{13}{16}$ (R)	$11\frac{11}{16}$	O	
$3\frac{3}{5} \times 4\frac{3}{8}$	=	$15\frac{3}{4}$ (E)	$15\frac{1}{4}$	O	
$6\frac{5}{9} \times 3\frac{3}{5}$	=	$23\frac{3}{5}$ (F)	$23\frac{1}{5}$	U	
$2\frac{2}{3} \times 5\frac{13}{16}$	=	$15\frac{1}{3}$ N	$15\frac{1}{2}$	(L)	
$3\frac{1}{2} \times 2\frac{5}{12}$	=	$7\frac{23}{42}$ Q	$7\frac{25}{42}$	(Y)	
$4\frac{4}{5} \times 3\frac{3}{4}$	=	18 (I)	17	T	
$2\frac{1}{3} \times 3\frac{3}{4}$	=	$8\frac{3}{4}$ (N)	$8\frac{1}{3}$	P	
$3\frac{1}{3} \times 2\frac{3}{4}$	=	$9\frac{5}{6}$ S	$9\frac{1}{6}$	(G)	

SUPER,
NOW
YOU'RE
FLYING.

MULTIPLYING FRACTIONS
Multiply. Reduce to lowest terms.

Name_____

1. $2\frac{2}{3} \times 3\frac{1}{4} =$
$\frac{8}{3} \times \frac{13}{4} = \frac{26}{3}$
$\frac{26}{3} = 8\frac{2}{3}$

2. $3\frac{7}{9} \times 1\frac{7}{8} =$
$\frac{17}{9} \times \frac{15}{8} = \frac{85}{12}$
$\frac{85}{12} = 7\frac{1}{12}$

3. $4\frac{2}{8} \times 5\frac{3}{5} =$
$\frac{34}{8} \times \frac{28}{5} = 23\frac{8}{10}$
$23\frac{4}{5}$

4. $4\frac{1}{3} \times 7\frac{1}{2} =$
$\frac{13}{3} \times \frac{15}{2} = \frac{65}{2}$
$\frac{65}{2} = 32\frac{1}{2}$

5. $5\frac{3}{8} \times 4\frac{3}{4} =$
$\frac{43}{8} \times \frac{19}{4} = \frac{817}{32}$
$\frac{817}{32} = 25\frac{17}{32}$

6. $6\frac{6}{7} \times 5\frac{2}{8} =$
$\frac{48}{7} \times \frac{42}{8} = \frac{18}{4}$
$\frac{18}{4} = 4\frac{1}{2}$

7. $5 \times \frac{20}{100} =$
$\frac{20}{20}$
1

8. $3\frac{1}{5} \times 2\frac{1}{8} =$
$\frac{16}{5} \times \frac{17}{8} = \frac{34}{5}$
$\frac{34}{5} = 6\frac{4}{5}$

9. $\frac{4}{7} \times \frac{14}{20} =$
$\frac{2}{5}$

10. $9\frac{3}{4} \times 5\frac{1}{3} =$
$\frac{39}{4} \times \frac{16}{3} =$
52

11. $2\frac{1}{2} \times 1\frac{1}{3} =$
$\frac{5}{2} \times \frac{4}{3} = \frac{10}{3}$
$\frac{10}{3} = 3\frac{1}{3}$

12. $4 \times 2\frac{1}{3} =$
$4 \times \frac{7}{3} = \frac{28}{3}$
$\frac{28}{3} = 9\frac{1}{3}$

13. $2\frac{3}{4} \times 5\frac{1}{3} =$
$\frac{11}{4} \times \frac{16}{3} = \frac{44}{3}$
$\frac{44}{3} = 14\frac{2}{3}$

14. $1\frac{9}{10} \times 1\frac{1}{4} =$
$\frac{19}{10} \times \frac{5}{4} = \frac{19}{8}$
$\frac{19}{8} = 2\frac{3}{8}$

15. $3\frac{4}{8} \times 5\frac{3}{7} =$
$\frac{28}{8} \times \frac{38}{7} = \frac{76}{4}$
$\frac{76}{4} = 19$

16. $6\frac{1}{4} \times 3\frac{2}{5} =$
$\frac{25}{4} \times \frac{17}{5} = \frac{85}{4}$
$\frac{85}{4} = 21\frac{4}{4}$

17. $5\frac{3}{5} \times 2\frac{6}{7} =$
$\frac{28}{5} \times \frac{20}{7} =$
16

18. $5\frac{5}{8} \times 4\frac{2}{9} =$
$\frac{45}{8} \times \frac{38}{9} = \frac{285}{12}$
$\frac{285}{12} = 23\frac{3}{4}$

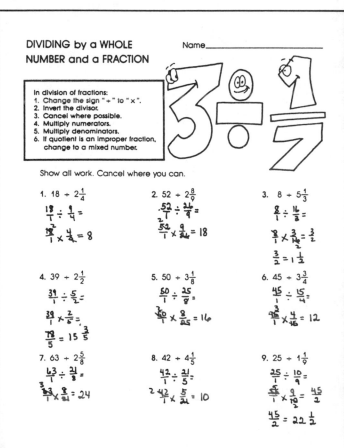

DIVIDING a WHOLE NUMBER by a FRACTION

Name_____

$6 \div \frac{1}{4}$	
$\frac{6}{1} \div \frac{1}{4}$	Step - 1
$\frac{6}{1} \times \frac{4}{1}$	Step - 2
$\frac{24}{1}$	Step - 3
24	Step - 4

1. $7 \div \frac{1}{3}$
$\frac{7}{1} \div \frac{1}{3} =$
$\frac{7}{1} \times \frac{3}{1} =$
$\frac{21}{1} = 21$

2. $8 \div \frac{1}{2}$
$\frac{8}{1} \div \frac{1}{2} =$
$\frac{8}{1} \times \frac{2}{1} =$
$\frac{16}{1} = 16$

3. $16 \div \frac{1}{3}$
$\frac{16}{1} \div \frac{1}{3} =$
$\frac{16}{1} \times \frac{3}{1} =$
$\frac{48}{1} = 48$

4. $6 \div \frac{1}{2}$
$\frac{6}{1} \div \frac{1}{2} =$
$\frac{6}{1} \times \frac{2}{1} =$
$\frac{12}{1} = 12$

5. $5 \div \frac{1}{6}$
$\frac{5}{1} \div \frac{1}{6} =$
$\frac{5}{1} \times \frac{6}{1} =$
$\frac{30}{1} = 30$

6. $18 \div \frac{1}{7}$
$\frac{18}{1} \div \frac{1}{7} =$
$\frac{18}{1} \times \frac{7}{1} =$
$\frac{126}{1} = 126$

7. $8 \div \frac{1}{5}$
$\frac{8}{1} \div \frac{1}{5} =$
$\frac{8}{1} \times \frac{5}{1} =$
$\frac{40}{1} = 40$

8. $7 \div \frac{1}{9}$
$\frac{7}{1} \div \frac{1}{9} =$
$\frac{7}{1} \times \frac{9}{1} =$
$\frac{63}{1} = 63$

9. $15 \div \frac{1}{6}$
$\frac{15}{1} \div \frac{1}{6} =$
$\frac{15}{1} \times \frac{6}{1} =$
$\frac{90}{1} = 90$

DIVIDING by a WHOLE NUMBER and a FRACTION

Name_____

In division of fractions:
1. Change the sign "÷" to "×".
2. Invert the divisor.
3. Cancel where possible.
4. Multiply numerators.
5. Multiply denominators.
6. If quotient is an improper fraction, change to a mixed number.

Show all work. Cancel where you can.

1. $18 \div 2\frac{1}{4}$
$\frac{18}{1} \div \frac{9}{4} =$
$\frac{18}{1} \times \frac{4}{9} = 8$

2. $52 \div 2\frac{8}{9}$
$\frac{52}{1} \div \frac{26}{9} =$
$\frac{52}{1} \times \frac{9}{26} = 18$

3. $8 \div 5\frac{1}{3}$
$\frac{8}{1} \div \frac{16}{3} =$
$\frac{8}{1} \times \frac{3}{16} = \frac{3}{2}$
$\frac{3}{2} = 1\frac{1}{2}$

4. $39 \div 2\frac{1}{2}$
$\frac{39}{1} \div \frac{5}{2} =$
$\frac{39}{1} \times \frac{2}{5} =$
$\frac{78}{5} = 15\frac{3}{5}$

5. $50 \div 3\frac{1}{8}$
$\frac{50}{1} \div \frac{25}{8} =$
$\frac{50}{1} \times \frac{8}{25} = 16$

6. $45 \div 3\frac{3}{4}$
$\frac{45}{1} \div \frac{15}{4} =$
$\frac{45}{1} \times \frac{4}{15} = 12$

7. $63 \div 2\frac{5}{8}$
$\frac{63}{1} \div \frac{21}{8} =$
$\frac{63}{1} \times \frac{8}{21} = 24$

8. $42 \div 4\frac{1}{5}$
$\frac{42}{1} \div \frac{21}{5} =$
$\frac{42}{1} \times \frac{5}{21} = 10$

9. $25 \div 1\frac{1}{9}$
$\frac{25}{1} \div \frac{10}{9} =$
$\frac{25}{1} \times \frac{9}{10} = \frac{45}{2}$
$\frac{45}{2} = 22\frac{1}{2}$

DIVIDING FRACTIONS

Name_____

Work problems. Shade boxes with whole number.

$\frac{4}{5} \div \frac{2}{5}$
$\frac{4}{5} \div \frac{2}{5} = \frac{28}{10} = 2$

$1\frac{1}{2} \div 18$
$\frac{3}{2} \cdot \frac{1}{18} = \frac{3}{36} = \frac{1}{12}$

$0 \div \frac{2}{3} = 0$

$\frac{1}{2} \div \frac{1}{4}$
$\frac{1}{2} \times \frac{4}{1} = 2$

$\frac{9}{10} \div \frac{1}{5}$
$\frac{9}{10} \cdot \frac{5}{1} = \frac{45}{10}$

$6 \div \frac{6}{7}$
$\frac{6}{1} \times \frac{7}{6} = 7$

$1 \div 7\frac{1}{2}$
$1 \cdot \frac{2}{15} = \frac{2}{15}$

$4\frac{1}{2} \div 18$

$\frac{1}{4}$

$4\frac{1}{2} \div 18$

$\frac{1}{4} \div \frac{2}{5}$

$5/8$

$4\frac{2}{5} \div \frac{1}{4}$
$22 \cdot \frac{4}{5} \cdot \frac{1}{1} = \frac{88}{5}$
$17\frac{3}{5}$

$\frac{1}{2} \times \frac{1}{2}$
2

$\frac{29}{64}$

$\frac{2}{3} \div 8$

$3\frac{5}{8} \div 8$

$3\frac{2}{5} \div \frac{2}{3}$
$\frac{17}{5} \cdot \frac{3}{2} = 5\frac{1}{10}$

$4\frac{1}{3} \div 1$
$\frac{13}{3}$ $4\frac{1}{3}$

$\frac{2}{10} \div \frac{9}{10}$
$= 1$

$\frac{1}{12}$

$1\frac{1}{8}$

$6 \div \frac{6}{7}$
$\frac{6}{1} \div \frac{13}{2}$

$3\frac{5}{8} \div 1$
$3\frac{5}{8}$

$1 \div 7\frac{1}{3}$
$\frac{3}{22}$

$\frac{4}{5} \div \frac{1}{12}$
6

Answer Key

Page 73

DIVIDING FRACTIONS   Name_____

Work problems. Arrange your work this way:

$$6 \div \frac{1}{4} = \frac{6}{1} \div \frac{1}{4} = \frac{6}{1} \times \frac{4}{1} = \frac{24}{1} = 24$$

$7 \div \frac{1}{3} = \frac{7}{1} \div \frac{1}{3} = \frac{7}{1} \times \frac{3}{1} = \frac{21}{1} = 21$	$8 \div \frac{1}{2} = \frac{8}{1} \div \frac{1}{2} = \frac{8}{1} \times \frac{2}{1} = \frac{16}{1} = 16$
$16 \div \frac{1}{3} = \frac{16}{1} \div \frac{1}{3} = \frac{16}{1} \times \frac{3}{1} = \frac{48}{1} = 48$	$6 \div \frac{1}{2} = \frac{6}{1} \div \frac{1}{2} = \frac{6}{1} \times \frac{2}{1} = \frac{12}{1} = 12$
$5 \div \frac{1}{6} = \frac{5}{1} \div \frac{1}{6} = \frac{5}{1} \times \frac{6}{1} = \frac{30}{1} = 30$	$18 \div \frac{1}{7} = \frac{18}{1} \div \frac{1}{7} = \frac{18}{1} \times \frac{7}{1} = \frac{126}{1} = 126$
$8 \div \frac{1}{5} = \frac{8}{1} \div \frac{1}{5} = \frac{8}{1} \times \frac{5}{1} = \frac{40}{1} = 40$	$7 \div \frac{1}{9} = \frac{7}{1} \div \frac{1}{9} = \frac{7}{1} \times \frac{9}{1} = \frac{63}{1} = 63$
$15 \div \frac{1}{6} = \frac{15}{1} \div \frac{1}{6} = \frac{15}{1} \times \frac{6}{1} = \frac{90}{1} = 90$	$2\frac{1}{2} \div \frac{1}{2} = \frac{5}{2} \div \frac{1}{2} = \frac{5}{2} \times \frac{2}{1} = \frac{5}{1} = 5$
$3\frac{1}{9} \div \frac{1}{3} = \frac{28}{9} \div \frac{1}{3} = \frac{28}{9} \times \frac{3}{1} = \frac{28}{3} = 9\frac{1}{3}$	$5\frac{1}{4} \div \frac{3}{8} = \frac{21}{4} \div \frac{3}{8} = \frac{21}{4} \times \frac{8}{3} = \frac{14}{1} = 14$

The smallest answer is __5__. The largest answer is __126__.

Page 74

DIVIDING FRACTIONS by WHOLE NUMBERS   Name_____

Reduce to lowest terms.

1. $\frac{1}{5} \div 3$
$\frac{1}{5} \div \frac{3}{1} =$
$\frac{1}{5} \times \frac{1}{3} = \frac{1}{15}$

2. $\frac{5}{7} \div 15$
$\frac{5}{7} \div \frac{15}{1} =$
$\frac{5}{7} \times \frac{1}{15} = \frac{1}{21}$

3. $\frac{7}{8} \div 21$
$\frac{7}{8} \div \frac{21}{1} =$
$\frac{7}{8} \times \frac{1}{21} = \frac{1}{24}$

4. $\frac{3}{5} \div 12$
$\frac{3}{5} \div \frac{12}{1} =$
$\frac{3}{5} \times \frac{1}{12} = \frac{1}{20}$

5. $\frac{3}{7} \div 6$
$\frac{3}{7} \div \frac{6}{1} =$
$\frac{3}{7} \times \frac{1}{6} = \frac{1}{14}$

6. $\frac{3}{8} \div 6$
$\frac{3}{8} \div \frac{6}{1} =$
$\frac{3}{8} \times \frac{1}{6} = \frac{1}{16}$

7. $\frac{5}{7} \div 10$
$\frac{5}{7} \div \frac{10}{1} =$
$\frac{5}{7} \times \frac{1}{10} = \frac{1}{14}$

8. $\frac{5}{6} \div 15$
$\frac{5}{6} \div \frac{15}{1} =$
$\frac{5}{6} \times \frac{1}{15} = \frac{1}{18}$

9. $\frac{7}{10} \div 2$
$\frac{7}{10} \div \frac{2}{1} =$
$\frac{7}{10} \times \frac{1}{2} = \frac{7}{20}$

10. $\frac{7}{8} \div 14$
$\frac{7}{8} \div \frac{14}{1} =$
$\frac{7}{8} \times \frac{1}{14} = \frac{1}{16}$

11. $\frac{7}{9} \div 7$
$\frac{7}{9} \div \frac{7}{1} =$
$\frac{7}{9} \times \frac{1}{7} = \frac{1}{9}$

12. $\frac{1}{4} \div 3$
$\frac{1}{4} \div \frac{3}{1} =$
$\frac{1}{4} \times \frac{1}{3} = \frac{1}{12}$

13. $\frac{8}{9} \div 16$
$\frac{8}{9} \div \frac{16}{1} =$
$\frac{8}{9} \times \frac{1}{16} = \frac{1}{18}$

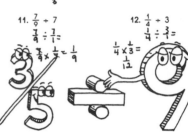

Page 75

PARTS of a SET   Name_____

Write a fraction to answer each question.

1. What part of this set of plants is a flower? __½__

2. What part of this set of drawings are squares? __¾__

3. What part of this set of containers is full? __⅙__

4. What part of this set of animals are cats? __⅔__

5. What part of this set of eggs are broken? __⅓__

Challenge:

6. What part of your class are boys? _____ girls? _____

7. How many dollars in $\$\frac{18}{6}$? __3__   In $\$\frac{30}{6}$? __5__

8. How many 6ths in 1? __6__

9. How many hours in $\frac{5}{12}$ of a day? __10__   In $\frac{7}{12}$ of a day? __14__

10. How many things in $\frac{11}{12}$ of a dozen? __11__

✻ Write five questions like the above ones on another sheet of paper.

Page 76

Work each problem, starting at the top of each machine, working down.   Name_____

32	51	73	99
× 65	× 56	× 80	× 1999
product 2080	**product** 2856	**product** 5840	**product** 197,901
+ 560	+ 6568	+ 24,685	+ 276,937
sum 2640	**sum** 9424	**sum** 30,525	**sum** 474,838
÷ 44	÷ 16	÷ 75	÷ 13
quotient 60	**quotient** 589	**quotient** 407	**quotient** 36,526
− 45	− 566	− 370	− 36501
answer 15	**answer** 23	**answer** 37	**answer** 25

15 + 23 + 37 + 25 = **Total** 100

Answer Key

Page 77

WRITING DECIMALS
Name_____

Decimals are names for fractional numbers. Write each fraction as a decimal.

1. $\frac{7}{10}$ = .7

3. $\frac{78}{100}$ = .78

5. $3\frac{2}{100}$ = 3.02

2. $\frac{2}{10}$ = .2

4. $38\frac{1}{10}$ = 38.1

6. $4\frac{36}{100}$ = 4.36

8. $\frac{4}{100}$ = .04

10. $8\frac{103}{1000}$ = 8.103

7. $\frac{3}{10}$ = .3

9. $\frac{21}{1000}$ = .021

11. $7\frac{16}{100}$ = 7.16

13. $\frac{2}{10}$ = .2

15. $38\frac{1}{10}$ = 38.1

12. $1\frac{8}{10}$ = 1.8

14. $14\frac{8}{10}$ = 14.8

16. $\frac{6}{10}$ = .6

18. $\frac{3}{10}$ = .3

20. $\frac{4}{10}$ = .4

17. $7\frac{6}{10}$ = 7.6

19. $15\frac{6}{10}$ = 15.6

21. $\frac{1}{4}$ = .25

23. $\frac{5}{8}$ = .625

25. $\frac{200}{400}$ = .5

22. $\frac{3}{8}$ = .375

24. $\frac{1}{40}$ = .025

26. $\frac{50}{125}$ = .4

27. $\frac{7}{8}$ = .875

Page 78

ADDITION of DECIMALS
Name_____

Add and check work. Keep columns straight.

1. .5 + .7 = 1.2

2. 2.5 + 3.8 = 6.3

3. 47.6 + 32.9 = 80.5

4. 85.6 + 9.7 = 95.3

5. .34 + .25 = .59

6. 3.91 + 4.23 = 8.14

7. 9.43 + 8.16 = 17.59

8. 72.9 + 83.4 = 156.3

9. 6.34 + 4.57 = 10.91

10. 24.39 + 8.70 = 33.09

11. 1.9 + .7 = 2.6

12. 343.8 + 9.6 = 353.4

13. 638.072 + 9.340 = 647.412

14. 921.063 + 72.430 = 993.493

15. 821.03 + 40.76 = 861.79

16. 726.435 + 814.291 = 1540.726

17. 72.413 + 18.943 = 91.356

18. 63.987 + 72.431 = 136.418

19. 814.2 + 72.6 = 886.8

20. 981.1 + 1.3 = 982.4

21. 926.723 + 72.631 = 999.354

22. 87.876 + 63.591 = 151.467

Page 79

ADDING DECIMALS
Name_____

Add problems.

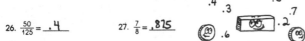

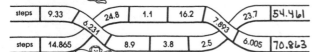
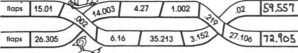
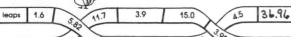
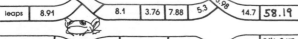
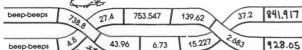

hops	.3	.4	.7	.3	.7	.4 → 3.8
hops	.2	.7	.8	.8	.3	.8 → 4
jumps	2.3	2.6	3.7	4.3	3.5	7.7 → 41
jumps	1.3	9.8 2.7	9.6	8.9	4.8 → 20.2
steps	9.33	24.8	1.1	16.2	7.823 23.7 → 54.461
steps	14.865	6.231 8.9	3.8	2.5	6.005 → 70.863
flaps	15.01	14.003	4.27	1.002	.219 .02 → 59.557
flaps	26.305	.002 6.16	35.213	3.152	27.106 → 72.905
leaps	1.6	11.7	3.9	15.0	3.98 .5 → 36.96
leaps	8.91	5.82 8.1	3.76	7.88	5.3 14.7 → 58.19
beep-beeps	738.8	27.4	753.547	139.62	37.2 → 841.917
beep-beeps	4.8	43.96	6.73	15.227	2.683 → 928.05

Page 80

ADDING DECIMALS
Name_____

Add center number to number in first circle to find the answer. Next, add all answers on wheel. Then, add all wheel answers to get total of all wheels.

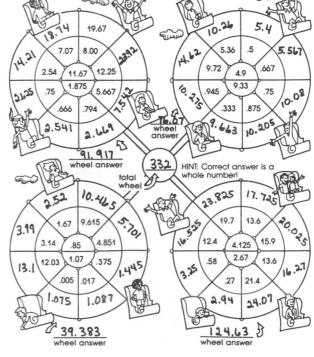

HINT: Correct answer is a whole number!

total wheel 332

wheel answer 91.917

wheel answer 39.383

wheel answer 124.63

Answer Key

Page 81 — ADDING DECIMALS

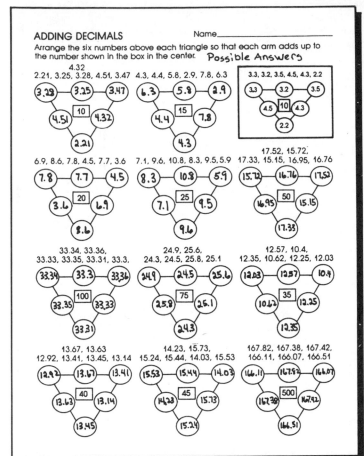

Arrange the six numbers above each triangle so that each arm adds up to the number shown in the box in the center. **Possible Answers**

Page 82 — SUBTRACTION of DECIMALS

Subtract. Check all problems.

#	Problem	Answer
1.	2.4 − .6	1.8
2.	.79 − .08	.71
3.	18.24 − 7.56	10.68
4.	38.57 − 16.83	21.74
5.	1.9 − .7	1.2
6.	13.5 − 7.3	6.2
7.	29.6 − 19.8	9.8
8.	42.6 − 8.1	34.5
9.	98.21 − 6.43	91.78
10.	2.7 − .7	2.0
11.	48.9 − 9.8	39.1
12.	63.29 − 9.43	53.86
13.	6.34 − 4.57	1.77
14.	12.6 − 6.5	6.1
15.	93.21 − 9.43	83.78
16.	691.98 − 42.69	649.29
17.	4.26 − .02	4.24
18.	98.6 − 7.8	90.8
19.	26.43 − 1.49	24.94
20.	987.23 − 8.97	978.26
21.	7.2 − 6.7	.5
22.	88.7 − 43.8	44.9
23.	95.7 − 8.6	87.1
24.	143.29 − 86.74	56.55

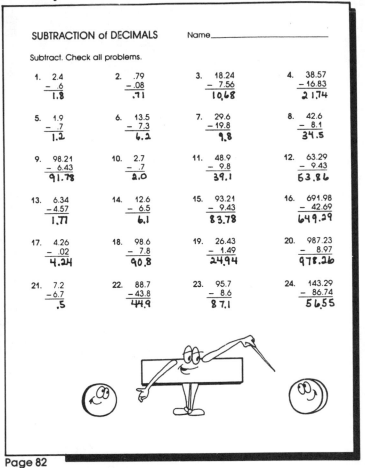

Page 83 — SUBTRACTING DECIMALS

Work problems. Use answers to name the kittens. Match names with answers. One is left for you to name.

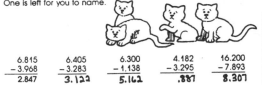

Problem	Answer	Name
6.815 − 3.968	2.847	Felix
6.405 − 3.283	3.122	Tinker
6.300 − 1.138	5.162	Ralph
4.182 − 3.295	.887	Smokey
16.200 − 7.893	8.307	
3.105 − .246	2.859	Coco
1.589 − .306	1.283	Harvey
9.200 − 3.032	6.168	Button
9.305 − 6.283	3.022	Tom
8.263 − 3.352	4.911	Kitti
117.52 − 74.25	43.27	Grover
6.895 − 4.174	2.721	Kat
8.975 − 1.017	7.958	Puff
16.206 − 5.359	10.847	Cleo
17.001 − 9.09	7.911	Oscar
8.495 − 3.653	4.842	Rocky
9.975 − 7.781	2.194	Sam
12.730 − 5.283	7.447	Morris
17.90 − 14.23	3.67	Angel
18.152 − 11.69	6.462	Sunshine

Name key:

Harvey	1.283
Puff	7.958
Ralph	5.162
Tom	3.022
Felix	2.847
Grover	43.27
Smokey	.887
Tinker	3.122
Cleo	10.847
Morris	7.447
Kat	2.721
Sunshine	6.462
Sam	2.194
Oscar	7.911
Angel	3.67
Rocky	4.842
Button	6.168
Coco	2.859
Kitti	4.911

Page 84 — SUBTRACTING DECIMALS

Work problems. The fisherman can only keep the larger fish, those with answers larger than 7.0. Put the problem number of the fish in the fisherman's basket.

Basket: 11, 15, 25, 16, 20, 26

How many were caught? **5**

1. .983 − .857 = .126
2. .896 − .277 = .619
3. .749 − .186 = .563
4. .864 − .173 = .691
5. 7.875 − 3.526 = 4.349
6. 6.685 − 1.845 = 4.840
7. 8.392 − 5.377 = 3.015
8. 8.879 − 2.892 = 5.987
9. 5.879 − 3.785 = 2.094
10. 5.786 − 3.493 = 2.293
11. 9.938 − 6.948 = 2.990
12. 2.796 − 1.385 = 1.411
13. .652 − .581 = .071
14. .954 − .763 = .191
15. 9.33 − .43 = 8.90
16. 26.2 − 13.8 = 12.4
17. 3.25 − .7 = 2.55
18. 9.23 − 8.2 = 1.03
19. 13.8 − 6.9 = 6.9
20. 42.61 − 32.6 = 10.01
21. 14.48 − 13.49 = .99
22. 14.5 − 9.7 = 4.8
23. 3.254 − .123 = 3.131
24. 29.263 − 24.35 = 4.913
25. 49.363 − 28.7 = 30.663
26. 27.258 − 4.1 = 23.158
27. 8.039 − 4.87 = 3.169
28. 1.760 − .157 = 1.603

Page 85

MULTIPLYING DECIMALS   Name_____

Work problems. Find answer and circle letter. Write letters in order for message.

4.98 × 100	=	4.98	B	498	(W)	49.8	H
2.6 × 10	=	26	(H)	26.	I	2.6	C
7.2 × 100	=	.72	I	720	(A)	7.2	G
.64 × 100	=	.64	P	6.4	G	64	(T)
.432 × 1000	=	432	(A)	4.32	W	43.2	G
53 × 10	=	530	(M)	5.3	F	.53	X
4.7 × 10	=	.47	V	47	(A)	470	F
3.1 × 100	=	310	(R)	3100	B	.31	O
100 × .02	=	.2	E	.002	C	2	(V)
100 × 4.82	=	48.2	T	.482	U	482	(E)
49.9 × 100	=	4.99	N	4990	(L)	.499	A
.0037 × 100	=	3.7	D	.37	(O)	.037	Z
.375 × 1000	=	3.75	J	37.5	S	375	(U)
1000 × .0036	=	3.6	(S)	.036	Y	.0036	X
6.005 × 1000	=	60.05	H	6005	(E)	600.5	C
29.5 × 1000	=	29,500	(F)	2.95	K	.0295	L
100 × .003	=	3.	K	.3	(F)	.03	P
.372 × 100	=	3.72	E	.0372	Q	37.2	(O)
10 × 74.3	=	743	(R)	7.43	S	.743	V
9.67 × 100	=	.967	D	96.7	J	967	(T)

WHAT A MARVELOUS EFFORT!

Page 86

MULTIPLYING DECIMALS   Name_____

Work problems. Where you find an answer, put an X. Where you don't, put an O.

```
  4.9        52        5.4       .17
× .87      ×2.8      ×7.3      ×5.6
 343        416      162       102
3920        104      378        85
4.263     145.6     39.42      .952

  .49        .40       9.1       7.7
× .78      ×2.8      ×.18      ×37
 392        320       728       539
343          80        91       231
.3822     1.120     1.638    284.9

  8.6        2.5        54        .62
×2.4       ×3.5      ×.92       ×83
 344        125       108        186
 172         75       486        496
20.64      8.75      49.68      51.46

  .47        9.5       .58        5.6
×.96       ×.74      ×.15       ×4.8
 282        390       290        448
423         665        58        224
.4512     7.030     .0870      26.88

  .867      90.6      3.72       44.5
× 48       ×.24      ×2.9       ×6.1
6936       3624      3348        445
3468       1812       744       2670
41.616    21.744    10.788    271.45

  .843      72.4
× .57      × 3.7
5901       5068
4215       2172
.48051    267.88
```

How many games did each win?
2 0 3

(tic-tac-toe grids with answers and X/O marks)

Page 87

MULTIPLYING DECIMALS   Name_____

Work problems. Use answers to guide coloring of design.

```
green         blue          red
  .463        28.5          6.51
×  82        × 7.4        ×  6.9
 926         1140          5859
3704         1995          3906
37.966      210.90        44.919

yellow        purple        purple
 39.2         7.54          .670
× .36        × .43        × .94
2352         2262          2680
1176         3016          6030
14.112      3.2422        .62980

yellow        yellow        purple
 64.9         .592          7.46
×3.26        ×40.6        × 5.9
3894         3552          6714
1298         23680         3730
1947         24.0352      44.014
211.574

green   blue   blue   green   purple  green   blue
 92.4   32.8   85.1   7.32   6.05    3.27    5.56
× .62   × .26  × .95  × 1.6  × 8.3   × .844  ×3.94
1848    1968   4255   4392   1815    1308    2224
5544    656    7659   732    4840    1308    5004
57.288  8.528  80.845 11.712 50.215  2616    1668
                                     2759.88 21.9064

yellow  red    red    red    yellow  yellow  yellow  yellow
 80.5   5.77   95.8   .784   2.57    29.3    6.80    .245
× .276  ×4.26  ×7.41  ×6.92  ×63.6   × .487  × .42   × 3.6
4830    3462   958    1568   1542    2051    1360    1470
5635    1154   3832   7056   771     2344    2720    735
1610    2308   6706   4704   1542    1172    28560   .8820
22.2180 24.5802 709.878 5.42528 163.452 14.2691
```

(star/compass design with answers: 80.845, 8.528, 37.966, 11.712, 57.288, 2759.88, 210.90, 21.9064 and inner labels b, y, g, p and values 163.452, 50.215, .62980, 22.2180, 44.014, 14.112 etc.)

Page 88

DECIMAL REVIEW   Name_____

Work problems. Shade in each answer to find the path to the bug

```
   .43       35.1       377.5      4.289      13.190
   .06      475.11    × 1.53     × 67.3     − 5.734
   .28        .54      11325      12867       7.456
   .77        .3       18875      30023
 + 1.01     + 1.5      3775       25734
   2.55      512.55    377.875   288.6497

  .4392      5.03       8627       5.621      3.108
× .216        .371    × 456      × 4.87     × .539
26352        .51       51762      39347      27972
4392         1.22      43135      44968      9324
8784       + 1.3       34508      22484      15540
.0948672    8.431      .3933912   27.37427   1.675212

 10.3500     5.764      8879       3.6        13.066
− 2.3844   + .49      − 2933     + 6.938    − 4.214
  7.9656    6.254      5.946      10.538     8.852
```

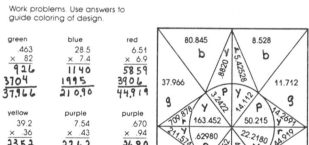

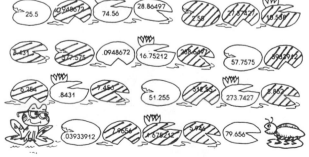

(lily pad path with values: 25.5, .0948672, 74.56, 28.86497, 7.58, 8.431, 37.375, .0948672, 16.75212, 57.7575, 6.254, .8431, 51.255, 273.7427, .03933912, 79.656)

Answer Key

DIVIDING BY A DECIMAL   Name_____

Work problems. Unscramble the letters to find the secret message.

M $2.1\overline{)8.4}$ = $21.\overline{)84.}$ → 4 = 4

A $0.36\overline{)1.872}$ → 5.2

S $1.24\overline{)0.4712}$ → .38

R $8\overline{)1.12}$ → .14

R $0.3\overline{)17.7}$ → 59

L $6\overline{)126.}$ → 21

A $.80\overline{)16.00}$ → 20

E $6.1\overline{)32.33}$ → 5.3

A $0.3\overline{)0.234}$ → .78

E $082\overline{)0.3772}$ → 4.6

H $0.2\overline{)6.34}$ → 31.7

C $9\overline{)81.9}$ → 9.1

D $7.4\overline{)103.6}$ → 14.

D $.87\overline{).5307}$ → .61

I $5.5\overline{)3.025}$ → .55

DECIMALS ARE HARD!

Page 89

WRITING DECIMALS AS PERCENTS   Name_____

To write a decimal as a percent, move the decimal two places to the right and add a % sign.

.95	95%	.02	2%
7.21	721%	2.5	250%
.08	8%	.156	15.6%
3.25	325%	.05	5%
.6	60%	.09	9%
.1576	15.76%	.88	88%
9.25	925%	42.5	4250%
.4	40%	9.21	921%
.12	12%	.8	80%
1.90	190%	.42	42%
.240	24%	1.00	100%
.60	60%	.63	63%
.03	3%	1.21	121%
.56	56%	.9	90%
.609	60.9%	1.5	150%

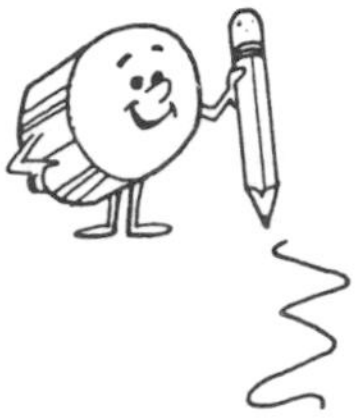

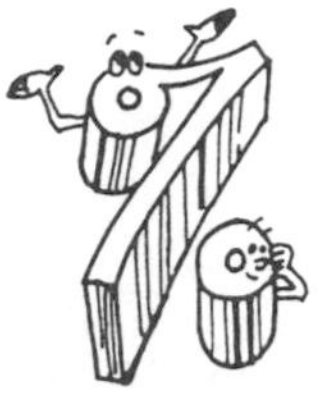

Rewrite the percentages in order, from smallest to largest. 2%, 3%, 5%, 8%, 9%, 12%, 15.6%, 15.76%, 24%, 40%, 42%, 56%, 60%, 60%, 60.9%, 63%, 80%, 88%, 90%, 95%, 100%, 121%, 150%, 190%, 250%, 325%, 721%, 921%, 925%

Page 90

BAR GRAPHS   Name_____

1. The bar graph below shows the number of problems each of five pupils had correct in a science test. Fill in each blank with the correct answer.

Christy
Joseph
Anthony
Latriece
John
Mary

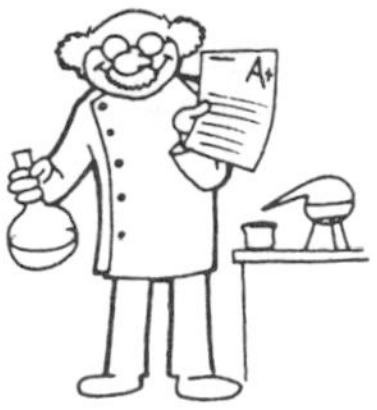

Fill in each blank:

Christy 6   Anthony 10   John 10

Joseph 9   Latriece 3   Mary 2

2. Show the weight of each boy in the sixth grade. Each square represents 10 pounds.

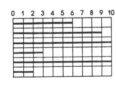

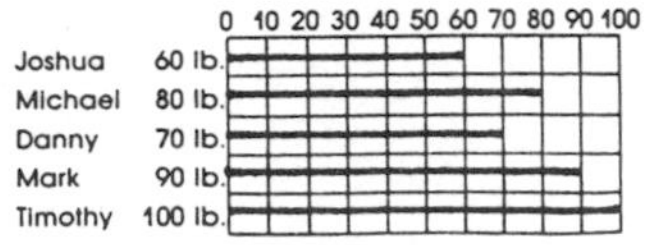

Joshua   60 lb.
Michael 80 lb.
Danny   70 lb.
Mark   90 lb.
Timothy 100 lb.

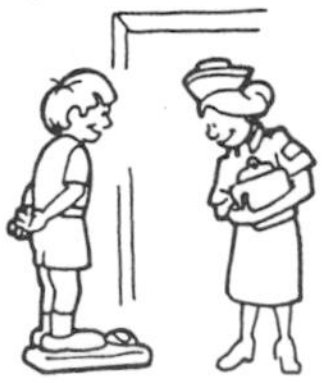

3. Challenge:
Make a bar graph showing your spelling test grades from last quarter.

 100%

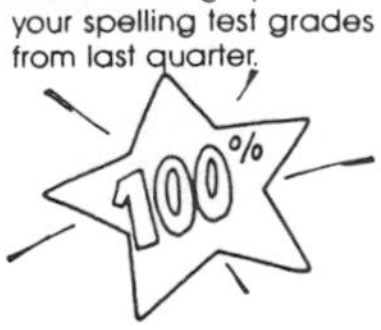

Page 91

MATH WORD PUZZLE   Name_____

Use clues to complete crossword.

Down.
1. ⊕
3. 3 ? 2 = 5
4. 2, 4, 6, 8
6. 3 ? 2 = 1
7. +
8. ▭
9. 1.5
11. −
14. >
19. ◓
20. 3, 5, 7, 9

Across
2. ×
4. =
5. $3\overline{)4}^{\,1\ R1}$
10. +
12. ○
13. △
15. <
16. 3 ? 2 = 6
17. 5 − 5 = ?
18. ½

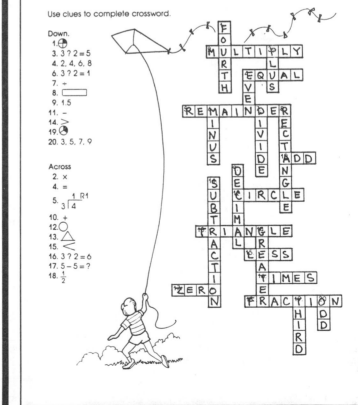

FORTH
MULTIPLY
EQUAL
REMAINDER
ADD
SUBTRACT
CIRCLE
TRIANGLE
LESS
ZERO
TIMES
FRACTION
THIRD
DECIMAL
RECTANGLE
DIVIDE
MINUS

Page 92

Answer Key

Page 93

MULTIPLE CHOICE
Circle the correct answer.

Example	a.	b.	c.	d.
1. 7481 − 3765	3,715	4,716	**(3,716)**	none of these
2. 86,107 − 59,476	**(26,631)**	27,631	27,632	none of these
3. $\frac{3}{4} \times \frac{5}{7}$	$\frac{12}{26}$	**($\frac{15}{28}$)**	$\frac{16}{29}$	none of these
4. 643 × 449	288,709	298,707	288,717	**(none of these)**
5. 5)547	6 r-37	9 r-38	12	**(none of these)**
6. 9 × 7 × 6 × 4	1412	**(1512)**	1612	none of these
7. $1\frac{1}{2} \div 18$	**($\frac{1}{12}$)**	$\frac{1}{18}$	$\frac{1}{2}$	none of these
8. 31)9362	202	**(302)**	301	none of these
9. $5\frac{3}{4} + 6\frac{1}{8}$	$10\frac{1}{2}$	$9\frac{7}{8}$	$8\frac{1}{8}$	**(none of these)**

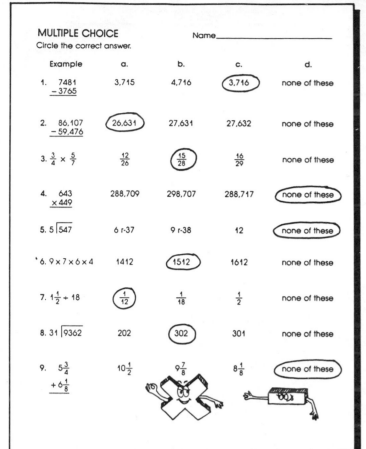

Page 94

AVERAGING
Find each class member's grade average. Also find the total class average.

	1	2	3	4	5	6	7	8	9	10	11	12	Avg.
Tanya	86	94	70	81	92	74	75	89	76	97	77	73	82
Noel		76	90	79	80	73	76	96	88	100	88	78	84
Greg	85		95	75	75	96		91	92			79	86
Todd	71	87	90	91	89		75	95	97	87	84	80	86
Brad		92		84	81		76	82		86	94		85
Richard	85	92	96		71		85	94	89	78	74	86	85
Parker	88	70	96	97		91	83		72	83	82	78	84
Ragon	93		73		82		78	93	77			85	83
Joey	90		98	78	81	94	74	73	98	79			85
Chris	72	93	87		83	86		93		72	88	82	84
Amber	100	90	98	77	90	70		95	91	82	87	88	88
Donna	71	96			83		92	92		88	94		88
Ed		89		95	100	72	75	92	81	79	82		85
Cora	84	88		92	88	93	80	89	100		89	77	88
Cheryl	74	79	86	98	84	78	100	80	85	81	84	94	85
Carrie	74		99	96		99	100	94	70		82	87	89
Ronnie	94	97	94	79		87		72	93	80	91	83	87
Steve	75	87	98	77	86	99	84	94	97	79	80	100	88
Fayne	76	86	100	73	87	94	81	90		87	91	81	86
Vernon	70	86	72		88	93	71		71		99	79	81
Sandra	77	88	98	88	79	96	82	89	78	100	92	89	88
Lee	82		76	75	85		98	71		77	80	76	80
Maureen	95		95	70		83	97	83	73	78	93	73	84
Tom		42		51	63		100		31		75	51	59
Ancil	97	77	70	81		92	83	88	74	90	80	70	82
Sue	83	83	74	74	74	87	82	73	76	84	94	88	81
Jackie	78		78		91	95				95	73		85
Nancy	96	80		96	72	94	84	86	74	98	96	70	86
Beth	79	71		82			78	85	76	77	99	100	83
Jan	70		86	82	75	80		92	95	81	76	93	83

Who has the highest average? **Carrie**
Who has the lowest average? **Tom**

84 class average

Page 95

AVERAGING
Find the average score for each group of numbers. Put answers on line below each group.

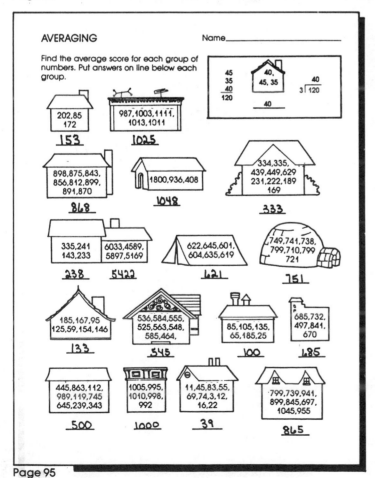

Example:
45, 35, 40, 40 / 120 → 40   3)120 = 40

- 202, 85, 172 → **153**
- 987, 1003, 1111, 1013, 1011 → **1025**
- 898, 875, 843, 856, 812, 899, 891, 870 → **868**
- 1800, 936, 408 → **1048**
- 334, 335, 439, 449, 629, 231, 222, 189, 169 → **333**
- 335, 241, 143, 233 → **238**
- 6033, 4589, 5897, 5169 → **5422**
- 622, 645, 601, 604, 635, 619 → **621**
- 749, 741, 738, 799, 710, 799, 721 → **751**
- 185, 167, 95, 125, 59, 154, 146 → **133**
- 536, 584, 555, 525, 563, 548, 585, 464 → **545**
- 85, 105, 135, 65, 185, 25 → **100**
- 685, 732, 497, 841, 670 → **185**
- 445, 863, 112, 989, 119, 745, 645, 239, 343 → **500**
- 1005, 995, 1010, 998, 992 → **1000**
- 11, 45, 83, 55, 69, 74, 3, 12, 16, 22 → **39**
- 799, 739, 941, 899, 845, 697, 1045, 955 → **865**

Page 96

ROUNDING
Shade correctly rounded answers to find the path to Skull Island.

9999 / 1000	7659 / 9000	6650 / 6000	239 / 300	9764 / 8000	4596 / 4000	9327 / 9000	3794 / 2000
3653 / 3000	8961 / 9000	5100 / 5000	4358 / 4000	6784 / 7000	59589 / 60000	3479 / 3000	6743 / 8000
7010 / 7000	3426 / 4000	7900 / 6000	4533 / 4000	9700 / 9000	1234 / 2000	6349 / 7000	4576 / 4000
2395 / 2000	1878 / 2000	5269 / 6000	2895 / 3000	16798 / 20000	1324 / 1000	55721 / 60000	57685 / 90000
9746 / 1000	3625 / 5000	3296 / 4000	5697 / 4000	7896 / 9000	4567 / 4000	8235 / 9000	27681 / 30000
92118 / 90000	7769 / 8000	66954 / 70000	(skull)	2975 / 1000	76950 / 70000	751 / 800	
63626 / 60000	237 / 300	5235 / 6000	(skull)	2975 / 2000	1099 / 2000	8479 / 8000	
31326 / 30000	1097 / 100	7659 / 7000	89657 / 80000	3974 / 3000	7695 / 9000	3265 / 2000	19618 / 20000
9191 / 9000	6253 / 7000	421 / 400	666 / 7000	4989 / 5000	965 / 100	7543 / 7000	396 / 400
7661 / 8000	8235 / 9000	92381 / 90000	367 / 300	23615 / 20000	73921 / 70000	52252 / 50000	36479 / 40000
333 / 300	3457 / 4000	553 / 600	6295 / 7000	4325 / 5000	9234 / 10000	765 / 700	4326 / 5000
793 / 800	42461 / 40000	77246 / 80000	3279 / 4000	1099 / 2000	4976 / 4000	7695 / 7000	6959 / 6000

Page 93

Page 94

Page 95

Page 96

Answer Key

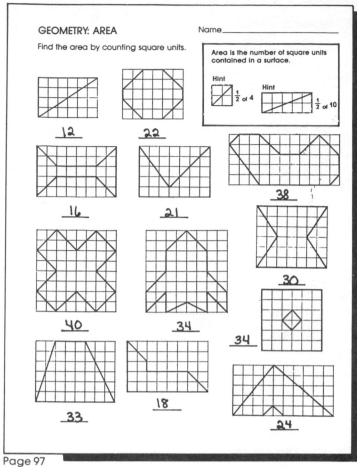

GEOMETRY: AREA

Name_____

Find the area by counting square units.

Area is the number of square units contained in a surface.

Hint: ½ of 4   Hint: ½ of 10

12   22

16   21

38

40   34

30

33   18   34

24

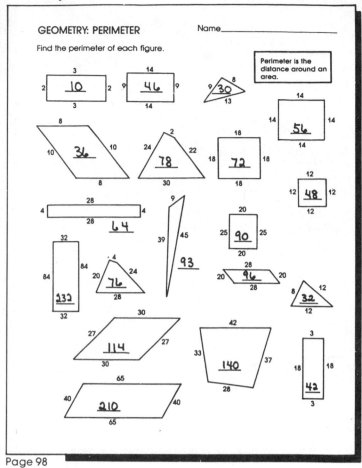

GEOMETRY: PERIMETER

Name_____

Find the perimeter of each figure.

Perimeter is the distance around an area.

10   46   30

56

36   78   72   48

64   90

132   76   93   96   32

114   140   42

210

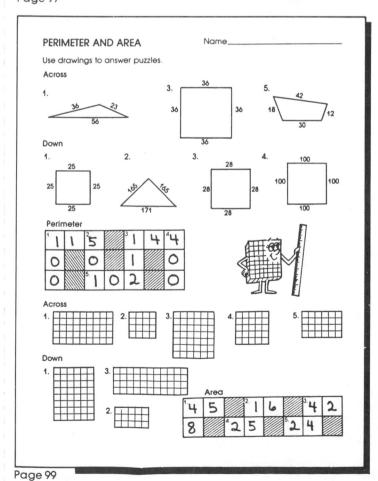

PERIMETER AND AREA

Name_____

Use drawings to answer puzzles.

Across
1. (triangle: 36, 23, 56)
3. (square: 36, 36, 36, 36)
5. (trapezoid: 42, 18, 12, 30)

Down
1. (square: 25, 25, 25, 25)
2. (triangle: 165, 165, 171)
3. (square: 28, 28, 28, 28)
4. (square: 100, 100, 100, 100)

Perimeter

1. 1	1	5	3. 1	4. 4
0		0	1	0
0	5. 1	0	2	0

Across
1. 2. 3. 4. 5.

Down
1. 3.
2.

Area

| 1. 4 | 5 | 2. 1 | 6 | 3. 4 | 2 |
| 8 | 4. 2 | 5 | 5. 2 | 4 | |

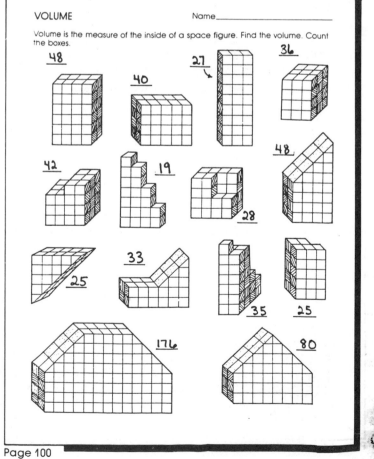

VOLUME

Name_____

Volume is the measure of the inside of a space figure. Find the volume. Count the boxes.

48   27   36

40   48

42   19

28

25   33

35   25

176   80

127

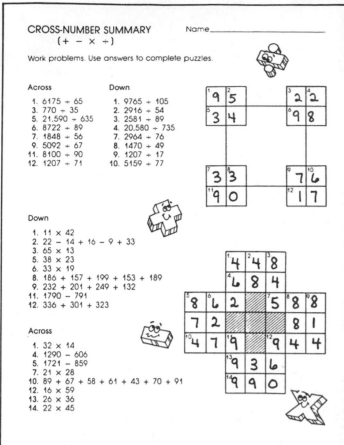

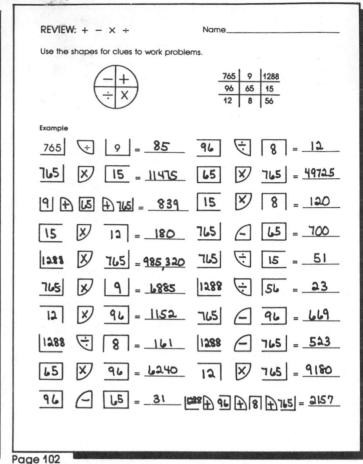

Page 101

Page 102

About the book . . .

This collection of activities concentrates on those very skills (basic facts, computation, place value, fractions, geometry, etc.) that the student needs extra drill and practice on to successfully master. A wide variety of approaches have been utilized whenever possible to stimulate interest and enhance motivation.

About the authors . . .

Sandra Bryan not only holds an advanced degree in Elementary Education, but has practiced the skills of the profession in the classroom for more than a decade.

John Potter is an experienced teacher at the elementary level who has taught kindergarten through sixth grade. His belief in an emphasis on basic skills is the key to his success.

Authors: Sandra Bryan / John Potter
Editor: Lee Quackenbush
Artists: Pat Biggs/ Phil Timper
Graphic Design: Julie Wiley
Production: Pat Geasler
Cover Photo: Frank Pieroni
Art Consultant: Jan Vonk